THE BEST OF
STAR TREK
THE NEXT GENERATION®

Michael Jan Friedman
John de Lancie
W R I T E R S

Pablo Marcos
Gordon Purcell
Matt Haley
Peter Krause
P E N C I L L E R S

Pablo Marcos
Carlos Garzon
I N K E R S

Robert Pinaha
L E T T E R E R

Julianna Ferriter
C O L O R I S T

Based on STAR TREK:
THE NEXT GENERATION
created by Gene Roddenberry.

THE BEST OF STAR TREK: THE NEXT GENERATION
ISBN 1 85286 526 1
First edition: March 1994
STAR TREK: THE NEXT GENERATION is a trademark
of Paramount Pictures. Published by Titan Books
Ltd, 19 Valentine Place, London SE1 8QH by
arrangement with DC Comics under exclusive
licence from Paramount Pictures, the trademark
owner. Copyright © 1994 Paramount Pictures. All
Rights Reserved. Originally published in single
magazine form by DC Comics as STAR TREK: THE
NEXT GENERATION 5, 6, 19; Annuals 1 & 2.
Copyright © 1990, 1991 Paramount Pictures.
All Rights Reserved. All characters, their distinctive
likenesses and related indicia featured in this
publication are entirely fictional.
Cover painting by Russell Walks.
Publication design by Veronica Carlin.

Printed in Canada.
10 9 8 7 6 5 4 3 2 1

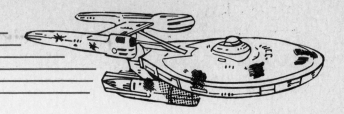

TABLE OF CONTENTS

THE STUFF OF WHICH
WONDERFUL, ROUSING STORIES ARE TOLD

"**I**'m over here working on *Star Trek.* Would you be interested in writing a script?"

These words, uttered by a friend of mine on the phone four years ago, changed my life. At the time, the call hardly seemed portentous — it was a possible job, that was all. And since I wasn't working at the time, I was only too eager to get the assignment; I'm restless when I'm unemployed.

I did have some misgivings: I was a *Star Trek* virgin. I'd never seen an episode of the original series. Never saw any of the features. Had scarcely *heard* of *Star Trek: The Next Generation.* I knew dimly of the existence of the phenomenon, and was vaguely aware of a cultish following of sorts. But I considered it something outside the mainstream of television; it was syndicated, after all, and was a science-fiction series (synonymous in my mind with "silly"). Wasn't it really just an overblown children's program? And didn't it have — anathema to a former English teacher — a grammatical atrocity in its main title (the split infinitive "to boldly go")?

Nonetheless, I told my friend Lee Sheldon that I'd look at the material. What could it hurt?

A packet arrived by messenger. It

contained two videotapes, several sample scripts, and a first draft of something called "Suddenly Human" which needed a rewrite. My task: to absorb all the material and decide if I wanted to do the rewrite.

My first realization that this series might be more than I had anticipated came when I watched "The Defector," a superbly produced and acted script by Ronald D. Moore. This was *good.* Then came "The Offspring," another unique and spellbinding story. I dug into the scripts: "The Bonding," "Hollow Pursuits," and "The Enemy." I was hooked. To my amazement, *Star Trek: The Next Generation* wasn't a silly science-fiction series — it was an intelligent, thoughtful examination of the human condition. It was about *people.*

The script to be rewritten needed a lot of

work, but at the same time was an absorbing story of a human child who is raised by aliens, then rediscovered by the *Enterprise* crew. A moral dilemma develops: should the child be reunited with his human relatives, or returned to the aliens and the only home he's ever known? This was subject matter I could dig my teeth into, and the script poured out of me.

On the basis of that rewrite, I was offered a staff position. Four years later, in the seventh and last season, I am an Executive Producer, responsible for running the writing department of *Next Generation*, developing stories and scripts, casting, editing, and making other creative decisions. I am the highest-ranked woman ever to have been involved in any of the *Star Trek* endeavors. And I consider myself one of the most fortunate people on earth.

It wasn't easy at first. I had to do a crash course in *Star Trek* 101 — watching t a p e s of all the (then) 80 episodes of *Star Trek: The Next Generation*, then the 79 episodes of the original series, and all the features. I used to take home four and five tapes a night, watching into the wee hours. My husband learned to say

"good night" immediately after dinner.

But the more I watched, the more I realized I had stumbled onto something special. This isn't news to all of you who are and have been avid fans, but to me it was a revelation. The power of Gene Roddenberry's vision, the captivating vision of a hopeful future, was overwhelming. Many of my personal beliefs — a united mankind, the possibility of an evolved consciousness — had been anticipated by Roddenberry, dramatized in a form that

appeals to some of our most basic needs and urges. *Star Trek*'s heroes are archetypes, and their goals are mythic: sailing into the unknown in search of adventure, engaging in a quest for knowledge, encountering and defeating terrifying demons, and bonding with one's fellows through it all.

Great stuff — the stuff of which wonderful, rousing stories are told. And that's the endless quest of the staff of *The Next Generation* — stories. They aren't easily come by.

I quickly discovered that the avenues to storytelling that are open to most contemporary drama series aren't available to us. I've worked on many such series, and usually it wasn't too difficult to get a story from (1) today's headlines, or (2) a contemporary milieu (ballet, rodeo, fashion modeling, etc.). We can't do that. Even if rodeos persist in the 24th century, they would have changed dramatically, in a way we would be unable to produce. And we can't really take stories right from the headlines; they're too readily identifiable as contemporary issues.

We have to scratch harder. If we deal with an issue (and we have, in some of our

most memorable episodes), we have to find an oblique way of addressing it, something that incorporates a science-fiction element that "turns it on its ear." Often we are able to find fresh new insights into the issue by doing this. ("The Outcast" is an example of such a story, one that allowed us to examine the issue of sexual intolerance in a unique, offbeat way. It is still the episode of which I am most proud.)

Our quest for stories is endless, and we tap all sources. Anyone can still write a speculative script for the show, and it will be read. We've found stories that way (including "Tin Man," "True Q," and "Gambit"). We invite writers to pitch ideas to us verbally; we take these pitches daily, sometimes two a day. We brainstorm among ourselves, sometimes going on a "retreat" (usually to my house) to get out of the office and put a fresh perspective on the creative

process. Sometimes we bubble with ideas; sometimes we sit and stare at each other glumly, devoid of inspiration. We never have more stories than we need.

Once we come up with one, we work hard on it, striving until the day it's shot to keep improving it, never settling for what's adequate, always searching for the thing that will make the story soar. Not all of them do. As with most endeavors, you win some, you lose some. Now and then, a few stories seem to capture magic, and all the elements come together in such a way as to become memorable. Our lists would probably coincide with many of yours: "Inner Light," "Darmok," "Yesterday's Enterprise," "Best of Both Worlds," "I, Borg," "The Host," "Cause and Effect." The list, fortunately, *could* go on and on.

Why the magic happens is never clear. If

we knew, we'd be able to accomplish it every time out. But we all recognize the really good stories and hold them dear to our hearts.

The stories in this collection represent that kind of "cream of the crop." These are the best — the stories that have taken wing, that have touched the heart and the mind and the imagination. These are the kind of stories that drew me into the *Star Trek* universe four years ago, where I now reside happily, still searching for the unique idea, the fresh concept, the unexpected twist.

With stories like these, I can almost forgive the split infinitive.

(In addition to being *Star Trek: The Next Generation's* Executive Producer, Jeri Taylor has written numerous episodes. She also wrote the best-selling novelization of the two-part episode "Unification.")

"CAPTAIN'S LOG, STARDATE 43201.8. WE HAVE REACHED CASSIOPEIA DELTA SEVEN--ALSO KNOWN AS *SERAFIN'S PLANET*-- AFTER RECEIVING A DISTRESS CALL FROM THE PLANET'S FEDERATION COLONY.

"THE CAUSE OF THE DISTRESS CALL IS PAINFULLY OBVIOUS NOW. INTERNAL STRESSES ARE TEARING THIS WORLD APART, CREATING ALL MANNER OF NATURAL DISASTERS ON ITS SURFACE.

"IT IS REMARKABLE THAT THERE ARE ANY SURVIVORS AMONG THE COLONISTS, GIVEN THE ADVANCED STATE OF THE PLANET'S SELF-DESTRUCTION. BUT PERHAPS I SHOULD NOT BE SURPRISED...

"AFTER ALL, THIS IS A MOST *UNUSUAL* COLONY."

SERAFIN'S Survivors

MICHAEL JAN FRIEDMAN
WRITER
PABLO MARCOS
ARTIST

BOB PINAHA
LETTERER
JULIANNA FERRITER
COLORIST
ROBERT GREENBERGER
EDITOR

BASED ON *STAR TREK: THE NEXT GENERATION* CREATED BY *GENE RODDENBERRY*

UNUSUAL DOESN'T BEGIN TO COVER IT, SIR. THERE'S NEVER BEEN A BUNCH OF COLONISTS AS TOUGH AS THE SERAFIN'S PLANET GROUP.

TRUE, NUMBER ONE. NEITHER AS TOUGH NOR AS SELF-RELIANT. HAD IT BEEN ANYTHING SHORT OF A CATACLYSM, THEY PROBABLY WOULD HAVE PREFERRED TO DEAL WITH IT THEMSELVES.

NO DOUBT, THIS TOUGHNESS STEMS FROM THEIR ILLNESS. HAVING LEARNED TO DEAL WITH THAT, THEY'VE COME TO BELIEVE THEY CAN DEAL WITH ANYTHING.

OR ALMOST ANYTHING.

IT'S NOT THAT AT ALL, DOC. HOW SHE LOOKS, WELL, IT'S SOMETHING I HANDLE BETTER THAN SHE DOES.

SHE ALWAYS HATED THE WAY PEOPLE STARED-- OR TURNED THEIR HEADS.

IT'S JUST THAT I REMEMBER DAHLIA BEING SO BEAUTIFUL-- SO FULL OF LIFE.

I SYMPATHIZE, GEORDI--BELIEVE ME, I DO.

BUT YOU SHOULD UNDERSTAND-- SHE MAY BE MORE FULL OF LIFE THAN EVER. SHE HAS TURNED HER RESENTMENT INTO SOMETHING POSITIVE ON SERAFIN'S PLANET.

THAT'S WHAT HAS ENABLED THESE COLONISTS TO EKE OUT AN EXISTENCE ON THIS SAVAGE WORLD--TO SURVIVE WHERE NORMAL PEOPLE COULD NOT.

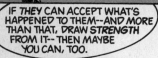

IF THEY CAN ACCEPT WHAT'S HAPPENED TO THEM--AND MORE THAN THAT, DRAW STRENGTH FROM IT-- THEN MAYBE YOU CAN, TOO.

I HEAR YOU, DOCTOR.

AND I WANT TO STAY.

TRANSPORTER ROOM! HAVE YOU GOT A FIX ON THE COLONISTS YET?

IT'S A BIT TRICKY, CAPTAIN. ALL THAT RADIATION AND...

WAIT! I'VE GOT THEM, SIR!

THEN BY ALL MEANS-- ENERGIZE!

⑤

MY GOD!

YOU CAN SAY THAT AGAIN!

DAHLIA, I...THIS IS A MIRACLE!

NO, GEORDI. NO MIRACLE.

BUT WE CAN TALK ABOUT THAT LATER ON...

YES--THAT'S RIGHT. WE'VE GOT TO GET THESE PEOPLE TO SICKBAY FOR A ONCE-OVER.

AND THE TRANSPORTER MUST BE FREED UP--FOR THE NEXT GROUP.

YOU NEED NOT HURRY ON THAT COUNT, DOCTOR...

THERE IS NO NEXT GROUP.

I STILL CAN'T BELIEVE IT, DATA. IT'S LIKE A DREAM COME TRUE!

JUDGING FROM YOUR BEHAVIOR, THAT MUST BE A POSITIVE DEVELOPMENT.

OF COURSE IT'S POSITIVE! I THOUGHT I'D NEVER SEE HER AGAIN--AND SUDDENLY, HERE SHE IS! ALL CURED AND EVERYTHING!

IF THAT'S NOT A DREAM COME TRUE, I DON'T KNOW WHAT IS!

IT IS NOT THAT I WISH TO PUT A DAMPER ON YOUR ENTHUSIASM, GEORDI.

IT IS ONLY THAT, NEVER HAVING EXPERIENCED A DREAM, I FIND IT DIFFICULT TO EMPATHIZE.

PERHAPS COUNSELOR TROI WILL BE IN A BETTER POSITION TO SHARE YOUR EXUBERANCE.

THAT'S OKAY, DATA. I'M SO HAPPY, I DON'T CARE IF NO ONE KNOWS IT--EXCEPT, OF COURSE, FOR DAHLIA!

LOOK AT THAT MAN, MOMMY. HE'S SO...WEIRD!

IT'S NOT NICE TO CALL PEOPLE WEIRD, RANDY. YOU MIGHT HURT THEIR FEELINGS.

DO NOT BE CONCERNED, MA'AM. IT IS NOT THE FIRST TIME I HAVE BEEN DESCRIBED THAT WAY.

NOR, TO BE ACCURATE, DO I HAVE ANY FEELINGS THAT MAY BE HURT.

I'M SORRY ANYWAY, MISTER DATA. YOU SEE, RANDY AND I ARE NEW ON THE SHIP AND... WELL, IT'S JUST THAT HE'S NEVER SEEN AN ANDROID BEFORE.

WELL, RANDY, HERE I AM. PERHAPS WE WILL HAVE AN OPPORTUNITY TO BECOME BETTER ACQUAINTED.

RIGHT NOW, HOWEVER, WE HAVE A MEETING TO ATTEND.

WOW!

8

AH-- THERE YOU ARE, GENTLEMEN. NICE OF YOU TO JOIN US.

SORRY, SIR. WE WERE... UM, UNAVOIDABLY DETAINED.

I'D BE INTERESTED TO HEAR ABOUT IT--LATER. FOR NOW, THE TOPIC UNDER DISCUSSION IS THE SERAFIN'S PLANET SURVIVOR GROUP.

DOCTOR?

PHYSICALLY, THE COLONISTS ARE ALL IN FINE SHAPE. I'M ALMOST TEMPTED TO SAY PERFECT SHAPE.

AND THERE'S ABSOLUTELY NO TRACE OF THE DISEASE THAT HAD AFFLICTED THEM.

SO FAR, HOWEVER, I CAN'T SAY WHY THEY'RE SO HEALTHY. MAYBE IT HAS SOMETHING TO DO WITH THE RADIATION THEY WERE EXPOSED TO WHEN THEIR PLANET BEGAN SPLITTING APART. MAYBE IT'S SOMETHING ELSE-- I JUST DON'T KNOW.

CAN THE COLONISTS THEMSELVES SHED ANY LIGHT ON IT?

THEY SAY IT WAS A FAIRLY RECENT DEVELOP- MENT--ONE THAT BEGAN TAKING PLACE ONLY A FEW MONTHS AGO. BUT BEYOND THAT, THEY HAVEN'T A CLUE.

9

WHAT ABOUT THEIR PSYCHOLOGICAL WELL-BEING? SURVIVOR'S GUILT AND SO ON?

FOR PEOPLE WHO'VE COME THROUGH SUCH TRAUMATIC CIRCUMSTANCES, THE COLONISTS SEEM REASONABLY WELL-ADJUSTED. HOWEVER...

I SENSE THAT THERE IS SOMETHING THEY ARE HOLDING BACK-- PURPOSELY.

HOLDING BACK, DEANNA? FROM YOU?

PERHAPS NOT FROM ME-- PERHAPS ONLY FROM THEMSELVES. BUT THERE IS ANOTHER LEVEL OF EMOTION THERE, AND I CANNOT SEEM TO REACH IT.

ARE YOU SURE ABOUT THIS, DEANNA? OR IS IT JUST A HUNCH?

PERHAPS IT IS MORE OF A HUNCH, AS YOU CALL IT, THAN A CERTAINTY. WHY?

YES, MISTER LAFORGE. EXACTLY WHAT ARE YOU GETTING AT?

10

I DON'T KNOW, SIR. WE SEEM TO BE DISCUSSING THESE PEOPLE AS IF THERE'S SOMETHING *UNTRUSTWORTHY* ABOUT THEM.

THEY HAVEN'T DONE ANYTHING *WRONG*, HAVE THEY? JUST *SURVIVED*. AND LAST TIME I CHECKED, THAT WASN'T A CRIME.

OF COURSE NOT. I DON'T THINK COUNSELOR TROI MEANT TO IMPLY THAT IT WAS.

NOR IS THERE ANYTHING WRONG WITH DISCUSSING THE SURVIVORS. THEY ARE, AFTER ALL, OUR RESPONSIBILITY--AND A MATTER OF SOME *LEGITIMATE* SCIENTIFIC INTEREST.

HAVE YOU ANY *OTHER* OBSERVATIONS, MISTER LAFORGE?

NO SIR. NO OTHER OBSERVATIONS.

11

BEEP!

YES-- COME IN.

I THOUGHT THAT MEETING WOULD NEVER...

OH-- HI.

SORRY, DAHLIA. I DIDN'T KNOW YOU HAD COMPANY.

THAT'S ALL RIGHT. I WAS JUST ABOUT TO LEAVE.

WELL? ARE YOU GOING TO STAND THERE FOREVER-- OR ARE YOU GOING TO COME IN?

12

I JUST CAME TO SEE IF YOU WERE ALL RIGHT. YOU KNOW--WITH EVERYTHING THAT HAPPENED...

YOU MEAN ABOUT THE OTHER COLONISTS--THE ONES WHO DIDN'T MAKE IT? I'M FINE-- JUST AS I TOLD YOUR COUNSELOR TROI. WE ALWAYS KNEW THAT SOMETHING LIKE THIS COULD HAPPEN. IN A WAY, I ACCEPTED ALL THEIR DEATHS A LONG TIME AGO.

BUT THERE'S SOMETHING WRONG WITH YOU--ISN'T THERE?

ME? WHAT DO YOU MEAN?

YOU CAN'T DECEIVE ME, GEORDI LAFORGE. YOU'RE JEALOUS--AREN'T YOU?

HEY, THAT'S OKAY. I SHOULD HAVE FIGURED THAT IN ALL THAT TIME ON SERAFIN'S PLANET...

I MEAN, WHAT- EVER HAPPENED THERE IS NONE OF MY BUSINESS.

YOU HAVEN'T CHANGED A BIT. YOU'RE STILL PLAYING THE ADULT--WHEN YOU'RE JUST A LITTLE BOY AT HEART.

13

DON'T YOU REMEMBER WHAT I TOLD YOU WHEN I LEFT FOR SERAFIN'S PLANET? THAT YOU'D ALWAYS BE MY BEST FRIEND?

WELL, THAT HASN'T CHANGED. YOU *ARE* MY BEST FRIEND-- EVEN AFTER ALL THIS TIME.

DUPONT DOESN'T MEAN ANYTHING TO ME. HE'S JUST SOMEONE WHO HAS GONE THROUGH WHAT I'VE GONE THROUGH--A FELLOW SURVIVOR.

THEN... NOTHING HAS CHANGED BETWEEN US?

NOTHING.

THAT'S ENOUGH, DATA. IT WASN'T *THAT* FUNNY.

ON THE OTHER HAND, I'M PLEASED THAT YOU UNDERSTOOD THE JOKE. AND *PROUD*, AS WELL.

IN FACT, I THINK THIS CALLS FOR A CELEBRATION-- ANOTHER ROUND OF SYNTHEHOL...

...WHICH I'LL SEE ABOUT SECURING FORTHWITH!

HELLO, ENSIGN.

HI, COMMANDER.

HI, MOM. ER...GOT A MINUTE?

WHY, CERTAINLY, WES. WILL YOU ALL EXCUSE ME?

OF COURSE, DOCTOR. A MOTHER'S FIRST RESPONSIBILITY IS TO HER SON.

16

WHAT ARE YOU LAUGHING AT, DATA? THAT WASN'T A JOKE.

AH--OF COURSE. SORRY-- MY MISTAKE.

HERE WE ARE. NOW...

WAIT A MINUTE-- SOMEONE'S MISSING. WHERE'S DOCTOR CRUSHER?

WESLEY REQUESTED HER PRESENCE AT ANOTHER TABLE, COMMANDER. WHERE-UPON THE DOCTOR LEFT US.

I SEE. WELL, DATA, I GUESS YOU'LL JUST HAVE TO CELEBRATE ON HER BEHALF.

17

BEFORE YOU SAY ANYTHING, WES, I WANT YOU TO KNOW THAT I'M GLAD YOU CAME TO ME WITH THIS PROBLEM.

WE HAVEN'T HAD A GOOD HEART-TO-HEART SINCE I RETURNED TO THE *ENTERPRISE*. I WAS BEGINNING TO THINK YOU'D GOTTEN TOO OLD TO CONFIDE IN ME.

ER... ACTUALLY, MOM, I DON'T *HAVE* ANY PROBLEMS. I WAS THINKING THAT *YOU* MIGHT HAVE SOME.

I MEAN, AFTER COMING BACK TO THE SHIP AND FINDING OUT THAT I'D... WELL, GOTTEN *OLDER*... AND MOVED OUT AND EVERYTHING...

I THOUGHT YOU MIGHT BE FEELING A LITTLE LONELY-- AND THAT YOU MIGHT WANT TO TALK ABOUT IT.

LET ME GET THIS STRAIGHT. YOU WANT TO HEAR MY PROBLEMS?

SURE, MOM. THAT IS, IF YOU WANT TO TELL ME ABOUT THEM.

MY LORD, WESLEY-- YOU *HAVE* GROWN UP!

(18)

EXCUSE ME.

I COULDN'T HELP BUT ADMIRE YOUR FORM.

IT IS KIND OF YOU TO NOTICE. I WORK HARD TO PERFECT IT.

BETAZOIDS ARE NOT GIVEN MUCH CREDIT FOR THEIR *PHYSICAL* ABILITIES. BUT LIKE ANYONE ELSE, WE ARE WHOLE BEINGS-- MIND AND BODY.

IS THAT WHAT YOU ARE-- A BETAZOID? YOU LOOK PRETTY HUMAN TO ME.

ACTUALLY, I AM *HALF-HUMAN.* ONLY MY MOTHER WAS A BETAZOID.

I APOLOGIZE FOR MY IGNORANCE. ON SERAFIN'S PLANET, WE PRETTY MUCH MINDED OUR OWN BUSINESS AND LET THE REST OF THE GALAXY GO TO BLAZES.

19

27

THAT IS NOT A VERY PRODUCTIVE ATTITUDE, MISTER URIBE. THE GALAXY IS FULL OF INTERESTING THINGS. SOME MIGHT EVEN SAY *WONDROUS* THINGS.

YES, COUNSELOR. I CAN SEE THAT.

AND I'M MORE GRATEFUL THAN EVER THAT I ESCAPED THAT MESS ON SERAFIN'S PLANET.

BECAUSE IF I HADN'T, I WOULDN'T HAVE MET YOU.

YOU FLATTER ME, MISTER URIBE.

NONSENSE. I CALL THEM THE WAY I SEE THEM. AND CALL ME MIGUEL.

MIND IF I SHOW OFF A LITTLE? I USED TO BE PRETTY GOOD AT THIS--THOUGH IT'S BEEN A LONG TIME SINCE MY BODY'S BEEN ABLE TO COOPERATE WITH ME.

WHATEVER YOU LIKE.

2

DAMN, THIS FEELS GOOD!

THERE! WHAT DID YOU THINK?

I AM IMPRESSED. I HAD NO IDEA THAT YOU HAD COME SO FAR IN YOUR RECOVERY.

NOR DID I. BUT AS LONG AS PROVIDENCE HAS SEEN FIT TO MAKE ME WELL AGAIN-- WOULD YOU HELP ME CELEBRATE MY GOOD FORTUNE? SAY, OVER DINNER TONIGHT?

I DON'T SEE WHY NOT. YOU ARE NO LONGER UNDER MY CARE AS A...

BEEP!

21

29

SORRY--I THOUGHT THIS WAS THE LOUNGE.

NOW WHERE WERE WE?

OH, YES. YOU WERE ABOUT TO ACCEPT MY INVITATION TO DINNER.

SWISH!

I JUST REMEMBERED-- THERE IS SOMETHING I MUST DO. PERHAPS SOME OTHER TIME...

22

GEORDI?

DEANNA--HI! WHAT BRINGS YOU DOWN HERE?

I NEED TO SPEAK WITH YOU--ABOUT THE SERAFIN'S PLANET SURVIVORS.

HAVE YOU NOTICED ANYTHING STRANGE ABOUT YOUR FRIEND DAHLIA'S BEHAVIOR?

STRANGE? WHAT DO YOU MEAN?

SHE'S NOT HAVING A RELAPSE, IS SHE?

NO, NOTHING LIKE THAT. I WAS REFERRING TO THINGS SHE MIGHT HAVE SAID-- OR DONE.

THINGS SHE WOULD NOT HAVE SAID OR DONE WHEN YOU KNEW HER BEFORE.

YOU'RE BEATING AROUND THE BUSH, DEANNA. IF SOME-THING'S BOTHERING YOU, COME OUT AND SAY IT.

23

31

JUST NOW, IN THE PRESENCE OF TWO OF THE SURVIVORS, I CAUGHT A GLIMPSE OF SOMETHING.

SOMETHING... I DON'T KNOW. VIOLENT.

YOU MEAN YOU'VE BEEN SCRUTINIZING THEM, AND NOW YOU FINALLY FOUND SOMETHING TO FUEL YOUR SUSPICIONS. IT SOUNDS TO ME AS IF YOU WANTED TO FIND SOMETHING!

GEORDI, THAT'S NOT FAIR!

IS IT FAIR TO GIVE THESE PEOPLE A HARD TIME--AFTER ALL THEY'VE BEEN THROUGH? CAN'T YOU JUST LET THEM BE?

OR IS IT JUST THAT I'VE FINALLY FOUND A LITTLE HAPPINESS--AND NOW EVERYBODY WANTS TO TAKE IT AWAY FROM ME?

EXCUSE ME, DEANNA. I'VE GOT A DATE-- WITH SOMEONE WHO LIKES TO SEE ME HAPPY.

SOMEONE WHO CARES ABOUT GEORDI LAFORGE.

GEORDI-- WAIT!

GEORDI!

TO BE CONTINUED!

THETA MARIANA FOUR. WE HAD SHORE LEAVE THERE ONCE, AND THE MEMORY JUST STUCK WITH ME.

IT SMELLS SO GOOD, TOO.

THE FRUIT TREES ARE RESPONSIBLE FOR THAT. THEY'RE CALLED *MIL'MARASSA.* LITERALLY TRANSLATED, *HONEY-FROM-THE-SKY.*

I BET THEY TASTE AS GOOD AS THEY SMELL.

THERE'S ONLY ONE WAY TO FIND OUT. CAN YOU GET ONE IF YOU STAND ON MY SHOULDERS?

I THINK I'LL JUST ABOUT MAKE IT!

CAREFUL, NOW! I DON'T WANT YOU FALLING AND BREAKING YOUR NECK!

OH, HUSH! YOU KNOW I'M TOUGHER THAN THAT!

THERE. JUST A FEW MORE INCHES...

ARRGH!

DAHLIA! WHAT'S WRONG?

UNNH!

ARE YOU ALL RIGHT? WHAT HAPPENED?

I'M FINE. I JUST HAD A... A MUSCLE CRAMP OR SOMETHING. BUT IT'S GONE NOW.

THAT'S SOME LOOK ON YOUR FACE! ONE WOULD THINK THE WHOLE SHIP HAD CAVED IN ON YOU!

I JUST GOT WORRIED, THAT'S ALL. I MEAN, WITH YOU HAVING BEEN SICK FOR SO LONG AND...

ENOUGH OF THAT, GEORDI LAFORGE. I'VE NEVER FELT BETTER IN MY LIFE!

AND IF YOU NEED PROOF OF THAT, TRY TO CATCH ME!

HEY! WAIT FOR ME!

3

ARE YOU CERTAIN OF THIS, COUNSELOR?

YES, CAPTAIN. THIS TIME I AM CERTAIN.

FOR A MOMENT THERE, BACK IN THE GYM, I GOT A DEEPER LOOK INTO THE COLONISTS' PSYCHES. OR, TO BE MORE PRECISE, THOSE OF DUPONT AND URIBE.

WHAT I SAW WAS A DESPERATE NEED. A VIOLENT, SEETHING HUNGER.

A HUNGER? FOR WHAT, DEANNA?

I DON'T KNOW, WILL. BUT IT WAS AWFUL.

4

THE COLONISTS CAME WITHIN A HAIR'S BREADTH OF DEATH--WATCHED HELPLESSLY AS THEIR COMRADES PERISHED. IT WOULD NOT BE SURPRISING IF THE EXPERIENCE HAS CREATED SOME SORT OF SUPPRESSED PSYCHOSIS.

WE TEND TO THINK OF THE SERAFIN'S PLANET SETTLERS AS SOMEHOW MORE DURABLE THAN THE REST OF US. BUT THEY ARE, AFTER ALL, HUMAN.

REGARDLESS OF HOW THEY GOT THAT WAY, IT SOUNDS AS IF THESE PEOPLE MAY POSE SOME DANGER TO THE REST OF THE CREW.

IF THAT'S THE CASE, CAPTAIN, WE SHOULD ALERT SECURITY--HAVE THEM WATCHED.

I AGREE, NUMBER ONE. BUT LET'S NOT BE TOO OBVIOUS ABOUT IT. IT WOULD BE CRUEL TO MAKE THEM FEEL LIKE CRIMINALS.

MISTER LAFORGE'S EARLIER POINT IS WELL TAKEN. THE COLONISTS HAVEN'T DONE ANYTHING WRONG.

AND THIS IS CALLED THE KIMBRIEL MANEUVER. IT IS A CLASSIC OPENING MOVE.

BOY, DATA. YOU KNOW MORE ABOUT SHARASH'DI THAN ANYBODY ELSE I'VE EVER MET.

THE PROPER RESPONSE TO THIS MOVE IS TO BRING UP ONE'S KAI'ELISKA TWO LEVELS...

RANDY?

DON'T TELL ME IT'S TIME FOR SCHOOL ALREADY!

THAT'S EXACTLY WHAT TIME IT IS. NOW, GET GOING, YOUNG MAN!

I'LL BE DONE WITH CLASS IN A COUPLE OF HOURS. WE CAN FINISH THE GAME THEN-- OKAY, DATA?

OKAY, RANDY.

IT'S VERY NICE OF YOU TO SPEND TIME WITH RANDY THIS WAY, MISTER DATA. I THINK HE UNDERSTANDS A LITTLE BETTER WHAT AN ANDROID IS NOW.

6

IT ALSO HELPS HIM FEEL MORE AT HOME HERE. IT'S NOT EASY BEING THE NEW KID ON THE SHIP.

AND SINCE HIS FATHER DIED, RANDY'S BEEN SORT OF WITHDRAWN. MAYBE THIS WILL HELP HIM OPEN UP SOME MORE-- MAKE SOME NEW FRIENDS.

THE PLEASURE IS ALL MINE, MRS. STOCKTON. I SELDOM HAVE THE OPPORTUNITY TO CONVERSE WITH ANYONE AS YOUNG AND ENTERPRISING AS RANDY.

WHAT IS MORE, RANDY AND I HAVE SOMETHING IN COMMON.

WE BOTH ASK A LOT OF QUESTIONS.

YOU KNOW, MISTER DATA, YOU REALLY ARE QUITE REMARKABLE.

YES--SO I UNDERSTAND.

ALL RIGHT, LAFORGE. WHY IS IT YOU DON'T BELIEVE THAT DAHLIA WAS TELLING THE TRUTH ABOUT THAT MUSCLE TWINGE?

CAN IT BE THAT SHE'S HAVING A RELAPSE-- AND SHE DOESN'T WANT TO ADMIT IT? NOT EVEN TO HERSELF?

MAYBE I SHOULD SAY SOMETHING TO...

HEY--WHAT'S GOING ON HERE?

THAT'S ONE OF THE COLONISTS-- ISN'T IT?

ARE YOU ALL RIGHT?

I'M FINE. REALLY I AM.

ENSIGN WEYLER--WHAT HAPPENED?

8

I DON'T EXACTLY KNOW, SIR. HE JUST GRABBED HIS LEG SUDDENLY, FELL DOWN AND BANGED HIS HEAD IN THE PROCESS.

IT MUST HAVE BEEN A CRAMP--HE WAS COMING FROM THE GYM.

A CRAMP. RIGHT.

WHERE HAVE I HEARD THAT BEFORE?

I BEG YOUR PARDON, SIR?

NOTHING. THANKS FOR THE INFORMATION, WEYLER.

DAMN! DAHLIA WAS LYING! AND SO WAS THAT OTHER COLONIST!

THERE'S SOMETHING GOING ON WITH THEM--SOMETHING THEY DON'T WANT TO FACE!

BUT THEY'VE GOT TO FACE IT--NO MATTER HOW BAD IT IS!

AND WHAT ABOUT YOU, LAFORGE? CAN YOU FACE IT--IF DAHLIA'S DISEASE IS COMING BACK?

YEAH. NO MATTER WHAT, I'M IN IT FOR THE LONG HAUL THIS TIME!

9

YOU KNOW THE VOW WE TOOK, MIGUEL. NO INVOLVEMENTS.

ESPECIALLY NOT NOW--WITH STARBASE NINETY ONLY FOUR DAYS AWAY.

SAVE IT FOR THE OTHERS, ANTOINE. THE ONES WHO CAN'T RESIST TEMPTATION-- AS I CAN.

COME NOW, MIGUEL. WE ALL FEEL THE NEED-- YOU AS WELL AS I.

AND TO TAKE A CHANCE BY GETTING CLOSE TO ONE LIKE TROI... AN OFFICER ON THIS SHIP...

IS WHAT, ANTOINE? FOOLISH? INSANE?

TO BE BLUNT, MIGUEL, YES-- ALL OF THOSE THINGS.

AND IF YOU WILL NOT CONSIDER THE PERIL TO YOUR- SELF AND TO US... THEN AT LEAST CONSIDER THE DANGER TO HER.

THERE IS NO DANGER TO TROI. OR TO ANYONE ELSE I CHOOSE TO CONSORT WITH.

ISN'T THERE?

10

HOW CAN YOU BOAST OF YOUR WILL POWER AFTER WHAT HAPPENED BACK ON SERAFIN'S PLANET?

HOW CAN ANY OF US MAKE THAT KIND OF BOAST?

THIS IS *DIFFERENT.* THIS IS *HERE--*NOT BACK ON THE PLANET.

WE ARE MORE *EXPERIENCED* NOW. WE *KNOW* WHAT TO EXPECT--WHAT TO *AVOID.* AT LEAST *I* DO.

IT'S *EASIER* NOW TO IGNORE THE NEED.

YOU'RE *WRONG.* IT'S NOT *EASIER* NOW-- IT'S *HARDER.*

COMPARED TO SERAFIN'S PLANET, THE *ENTERPRISE* IS A *PARADISE.* AND IN PARADISE, *TEMPTATION* IS *MAGNIFIED.*

JUST WAIT, MIGUEL. WAIT FOUR MORE DAYS AND WE CAN ALL DO WHAT WE WANT TO DO--WHAT WE *NEED* TO DO.

DAMN YOU, ANTOINE. HOW CAN YOU REMAIN THE VOICE OF REASON WHEN FATE HAS MADE YOU A *GOD?*

FOR *YEARS,* WE LIVED LIKE SOMETHING *LESS* THAN MEN. DON'T YOU *BURN* TO MAKE UP FOR THE TIME DENIED YOU?

YES. I DO.

BUT I CAN WAIT A LITTLE WHILE LONGER.

11

WHAT ABOUT DAHLIA? HAVE YOU SPOKEN TO HER, TOO?

OR DOES SHE GET SPECIAL TREATMENT?

NO-- DAHLIA IS NO DIFFERENT FROM THE REST OF US. I HAVE WARNED HER AS I'M WARNING YOU.

AND?

I AM CONCERNED ABOUT DAHLIA. EVEN MORE SO THAN I WAS ABOUT YOU, MIGUEL.

SHE, TOO, ASSURES ME THAT SHE CAN HANDLE WHATEVER SHE'S GOTTEN INTO. BUT I HAVE MY DOUBTS.

IN FACT, I WANT YOU TO KEEP AN EYE ON HER. TO WATCH FOR ANY... INDISCRETIONS, SHALL WE SAY?

AND IF I DON'T WANT TO KEEP AN EYE ON HER?

THEN BOTH OF YOU MAY WISH YOU'D BEEN BETTER AT KEEPING OUR VOW!

12

COVER-UP, GEORDI? WHAT DO YOU MEAN?

YOU KNOW WHAT I MEAN. I WANT THE TRUTH--AND I'LL STILL LOVE YOU, NO MATTER WHAT IT IS.

I TOLD YOU THE TRUTH. WHY THESE QUESTIONS ALL OF A SUDDEN?

SHADOWS IN THE GARDEN

DON'T PLAY INNOCENT WITH ME. I'VE BEEN STUDYING THE OTHER COLONISTS. THEY'RE ALL SUFFERING THE SAME MUSCLE CRAMPS YOU ARE--OR MANY OF THEM, ANYWAY. TOO MANY TO CALL IT A COINCIDENCE.

I LOVE YOU, DAHLIA. WHATEVER'S WRONG, YOU CAN TRUST ME.

HELL--YOU HAVE TO TRUST SOMEONE.

YOU'RE JUST JUMPING TO... UNNH!

DAHLIA!

YOU SEE? THERE IS SOMETHING WRONG WITH YOU!

13

IT'S THE DISEASE, ISN'T IT? IT'S COMING BACK!

NO, GEORDI. IT'S NOT THE DISEASE...

...IT'S SOMETHING MUCH WORSE.

IT BEGAN WITH THE FIRST UPHEAVAL ON SERAFIN'S PLANET-- MONTHS AGO, LONG BEFORE WE HAD ANY IDEA OF THE CATASTROPHE TO COME.

THE UPHEAVAL EXPOSED US TO RADIOACTIVE MATERIAL LYING JUST BENEATH THE SURFACE. IT CHANGED US. CURED US AND MADE US THE SUPERMEN WE ARE TODAY.

BUT EVEN AS IT CURED US OF OUR DISEASE, IT AFFLICTED US WITH ANOTHER ONE. FOR THE ONLY WAY TO MAINTAIN OUR EXTRAORDINARY METABOLISMS WAS TO DRAW OUT ENERGY FROM OTHER HUMAN BEINGS.

DRAW OUT... ENERGY? HOW?

DIRECTLY, GEORDI. ALL WE HAD TO DO WAS TOUCH SOMEONE AND CONCENTRATE-- AND THE LIFE-FORCE FLOWED OUT OF THEM INTO US.

14

BUT HOW COULD YOU KNOW THIS? UNLESS YOU...

THAT'S RIGHT...

...THE COLONISTS WHO SURVIVED WERE THE STRONGEST. THE OTHERS DIED YIELDING UP THEIR ENERGY TO US.

THEN IT WASN'T THE PLANET'S BREAK-UP THAT KILLED THEM.

NO, GEORDI. IT WAS US.

EVER SINCE WE CAME ABOARD THE ENTERPRISE, THE NEED FOR MORE OF THAT ENERGY HAS BEEN GROWING IN US--CAUSING THOSE MUSCLE CRAMPS YOU NOTICED.

AND WORSE--MUCH WORSE--

--EVERY TIME ANOTHER PERSON PASSES NEAR US...TOUCHES US... THE NEED IS ACCELERATED. WE ARE DOING OUR BEST TO FIGHT IT-- AT LEAST UNTIL WE GET TO STARBASE NINETY, WHERE WE CAN FEED WITHOUT FEAR OF BEING DISCOVERED.

BUT BEING NEAR YOU HAS MADE IT SO MUCH HARDER FOR ME. I THOUGHT I COULD HANDLE EXTENDED CONTACT WITH ANOTHER HUMAN BEING-- BUT I CAN'T.

THE NEED IS CONSUMING ME--KILLING ME. I CAN'T WAIT UNTIL WE REACH STARBASE NINETY.

I DON'T WANT TO HURT YOU, GEORDI-- BUT I CAN'T HOLD MYSELF BACK MUCH LONGER.

I NEED TO FEED ON SOMEONE SOON, OR I'LL DIE. HELP ME, GEORDI-- PLEASE!

15

DAHLIA--YOU DON'T KNOW WHAT YOU'RE SAYING. LET ME CALL DOCTOR CRUSHER--THERE'S GOT TO BE SOMETHING SHE CAN DO FOR YOU.

NO! NO ONE MUST FIND OUT ABOUT US! THEY'LL TREAT US LIKE MONSTERS-- DESTROY US!

YOU SAID YOU'D LOVE ME-- NO MATTER WHAT!

I DO LOVE YOU!

THEN PROVE IT! FIND ME SOMEONE TO FEED ON-- SOMEONE WHO WON'T BE MISSED!

NO, DAHLIA. I'LL PROVE IT BY CALLING SICKBAY-- BY GETTING YOU THE KIND OF HELP YOU REALLY NEED...

NO!

16

...HOOL ISN'T ...D, DATA. BUT ...IKE LEARNING ... PLAY ...HARASH'DI ...UCH ...TTER.

SHARASH'DI IS SOMETHING ONE MAY ENJOY *AFTER* ONE HAS ATTENDED TO ONE'S DUTIES.

AND IN YOUR CASE, YOUR DUTIES ARE YOUR STUDIES.

IN ANY CASE, I MUST GO UP TO THE BRIDGE NOW. MY SHIFT BEGINS IN THREE AND A HALF MINUTES.

AW, DO YOU *HAVE* TO?

I AM AFRAID SO.

CAN YOU AT LEAST TAKE ME UP ON THE BRIDGE-- TO TAKE A LOOK AROUND?

THE CAPTAIN IS NOT FOND OF ENTERTAINING YOUNGSTERS ON THE BRIDGE, RANDY. BELIEVE ME-- I KNOW FROM EXPERIENCE.

BUT WHEN MY SHIFT IS OVER, PERHAPS YOU CAN TELL ME MORE ABOUT YOUR STUDIES.

OKAY-- SURE.

17

49

SEE YA LATER!

HELLO AGAIN, RANDY. IT OCCURRED TO ME THAT YOU MIGHT WANT TO ACCOMPANY ME UP TO THE BRIDGE-- IF NOT ACTUALLY ONTO IT. THEN YOU COULD...

AH--MISS SANTORINI. HOW ARE YOU FEELING? GEORDI MENTIONED THAT YOU HAD EXPERIENCED SOME DISCOMFORT IN...

DAMN! WHAT HIT ME?

AND HOW LONG HAVE I BEEN LYING HERE LIKE THIS?

WAIT A MINUTE-- I REMEMBER NOW! DAHLIA MUST HAVE KNOCKED ME OUT AND...

OH, NO.

LAFORGE TO SECURITY! WORF, YOU'VE GOT TO FIND DAHLIA-- AND STOP HER!

I CAN'T EXPLAIN NOW--BUT SHE COULD KILL SOMEBODY!

SHE ALREADY HAS.

ENSIGN WEYLER IS DEAD.

OH, GOD! SHE REALLY DID IT!

DO YOU KNOW WHERE SHE COULD HAVE GONE?

19

20

I DON'T STAND A CHANCE AGAINST *ONE* OF THEM, MUCH LESS *THREE* OF THEM-- UNLESS I DO SOMETHING TO EVEN UP THE ODDS!

WHAT'S HE DOING?

THAT'S THE CONTROL PANEL! IT REGULATES THE BAY'S SUPPLY OF HEAT AND...

...LIGHT!

WHERE IS HE?

I THINK I HEARD HIM OVER THERE!

VERY CLEVER, LAFORGE. YOU'VE TAKEN AWAY SOME OF OUR ADVANTAGE.

BUT THERE ARE *THREE* OF US--AND ONLY *ONE* OF YOU. WE'RE BOUND TO FIND YOU SOONER OR LATER!

I'VE GOT TO KEEP THEM TALKING-- KEEP THEM FROM THINKING ABOUT TAKING OFF IN THE SHUTTLES!

Y DID YOU N ON DAHLIA? E WAS ONE YOU.

WE DIDN'T WANT TO KILL HER--WE *HAD* TO. HER LITTLE INDISCRETION WOULD HAVE GIVEN US AWAY--JUST AS *YOU* WOULD NOW, IF WE ALLOWED YOU TO ESCAPE!

21

53

BUT IF WE KILL YOU AND ARRANGE SOME SORT OF EXPLOSION--MAKE IT LOOK LIKE AN ACCIDENT--WE CAN STILL FEND OFF SUSPICION UNTIL WE REACH STARBASE NINETY.

AND THEN WE'RE HOME FREE.

NOT IF I CAN HELP IT. AND IN THE DARK, I CAN HELP IT A LOT.

OVERCONFIDENCE CAN BE FATAL, LAFORGE! YOU SHOULD HAVE STAYED IN A CORNER SOMEWHERE AND KEPT QUIET!

COFF!

DON'T MOVE!

I TOLD YOU NOT TO MOVE.

22

DOCTOR CRUSHER WILL BRING YOU AROUND, DAHLIA. YOU'LL SEE.

NO SHE WON'T, GEORDI. SHE'S ALREADY DONE EVERYTHING SHE CAN.

IT'S ALL RIGHT. IT REALLY IS.

I'M JUST GLAD IT'S ALL OVER.

DON'T TALK LIKE THAT, DAHLIA. DON'T GIVE UP.

YOU JUST CAME BACK-- HOW CAN YOU LEAVE ME AGAIN?

THEN THERE'S NO HOPE FOR HER?

NONE. IT'S A MIRACLE THAT SHE'S HUNG ON EVEN THIS LONG.

GOODBYE, GEORDI. I LOVED YOU.

I'LL ALWAYS LOVE YOU.

DAHLIA... PLEASE...

23

55

"There are shadows in the garden."

"Like us, they are the children of the sunlight."

"Learn to love them despite their darkness."

"For with the onslaught of night's greater darkness, they will fade and be forgotten."

--AN UNKNOWN VULCAN POET

DEANNA, HAVE YOU EVER THOUGHT ABOUT... YOU KNOW... THE END?

YOU MEAN DEATH? OF COURSE, BEVERLY. EVERYONE THINKS ABOUT IT AT ONE TIME OR ANOTHER.

IS THAT WHAT YOU'VE HAD ON YOUR MIND THESE LAST FEW DAYS?

SO YOU'VE NOTICED?

YOU KNOW MY TALENTS. HOW COULD I HELP BUT NOTICE--EVEN BEFORE YOU ASKED TO SEE ME?

YOU'RE NOT ILL, ARE YOU? IS THIS YOUR WAY OF TELLING ME THAT...?

NO, DEANNA, IT'S NOTHING QUITE SO GRIM.

ON THE OTHER HAND, I GUESS IT'S GRIM ENOUGH.

IS THAT ALL? SHAME ON YOU, BEVERLY. YOU HAD ME WORRIED.

WHAT DO YOU MEAN, IS THAT *ALL?* DON'T YOU HAVE ANY WORDS OF WISDOM? ANY COMFORTING ADVICE ABOUT GROWING OLD GRACEFULLY?

YES--I DO. BUT I DON'T THINK THAT'S WHAT YOU REALLY WANT--OR NEED.

INSTEAD, I WOULD LIKE TO GIVE YOU A BIRTHDAY GIFT.

OH, NO YOU DON'T. A GIFT IS ONLY GOING TO MAKE ME FEEL WORSE.

YOU'RE A COUNSELOR. CAN'T YOU UNDERSTAND THAT?

THIS GIFT IS DIFFERENT.

3

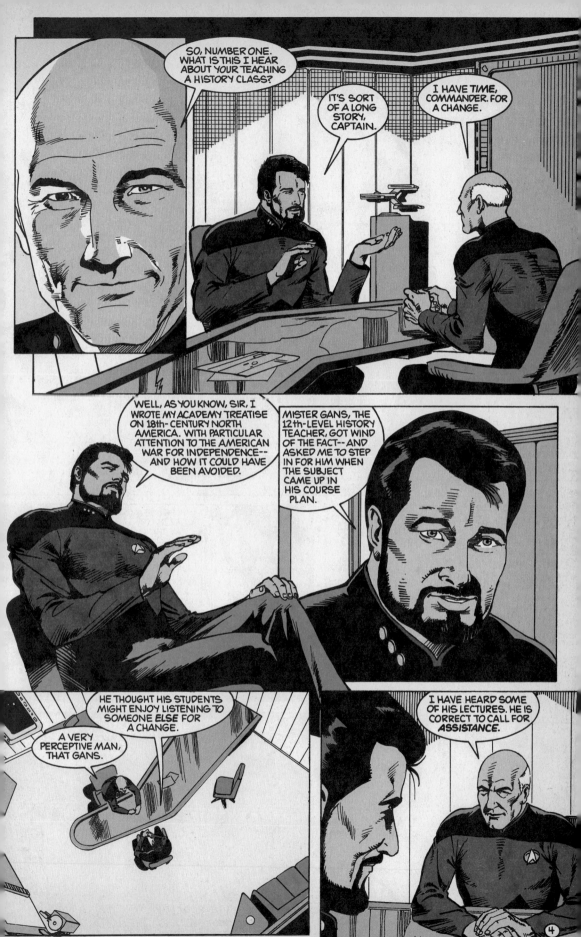

SO, NUMBER ONE. WHAT IS THIS I HEAR ABOUT YOUR TEACHING A HISTORY CLASS?

IT'S SORT OF A LONG STORY, CAPTAIN.

I HAVE TIME, COMMANDER. FOR A CHANGE.

WELL, AS YOU KNOW, SIR, I WROTE MY ACADEMY TREATISE ON 18th-CENTURY NORTH AMERICA. WITH PARTICULAR ATTENTION TO THE AMERICAN WAR FOR INDEPENDENCE-- AND HOW IT COULD HAVE BEEN AVOIDED.

MISTER GANS, THE 12th-LEVEL HISTORY TEACHER, GOT WIND OF THE FACT-- AND ASKED ME TO STEP IN FOR HIM WHEN THE SUBJECT CAME UP IN HIS COURSE PLAN.

HE THOUGHT HIS STUDENTS MIGHT ENJOY LISTENING TO SOMEONE ELSE FOR A CHANGE.

A VERY PERCEPTIVE MAN, THAT GANS.

I HAVE HEARD SOME OF HIS LECTURES. HE IS CORRECT TO CALL FOR ASSISTANCE.

4

HONESTLY, DEANNA. I WISH YOU'D TELL ME WHY IT WAS NECESSARY TO DRESS THIS WAY.

YOU WILL SEE FOR YOURSELF BEFORE VERY LONG. PLEASE TRY TO HAVE A LITTLE PATIENCE, BEVERLY.

THERE.

WHY DO I FEEL LIKE I'M BEING KIDNAPPED?

REALLY, BEVERLY. YOU MUST TRY HARDER TO EMBRACE THE SPIRIT OF THE THING.

I MIGHT BE MORE INCLINED TO DO THAT IF I KNEW WHAT THE THING WAS...

HMM. NOT A BAD JOB, IF I DO SAY SO MYSELF.

5

I LOVE YOU FOR THE THOUGHT-- I REALLY DO. BUT I DON'T HAVE THE TIME RIGHT NOW FOR--

NONSENSE! OF COURSE YOU DO!

DEANNA-- WHERE ARE YOU GOING? DEANNA?

HONESTLY, BEVERLY. DID YOU THINK THAT I PROGRAMMED JUST ONE LITTLE BIT OF FOREST?

WHAT KIND OF GIFT WOULD THAT BE?

HEY, WESLEY!

HI, ARI.

SO, WHAT'S THE WORD? IS COMMANDER RIKER GOING TO POP A QUIZ ON US AT THE END OF CLASS?

HOW SHOULD I KNOW?

COME ON, WES. YOU SPEND ALL THAT TIME UP ON THE BRIDGE, DON'T YOU? ARE YOU TELLING ME THE SUBJECT NEVER CAME UP?

THAT'S *EXACTLY* WHAT I'M TELLING YOU. BELIEVE ME-- THERE ARE MORE IMPORTANT THINGS TO DISCUSS ON THE BRIDGE THAN A POP QUIZ IN MISTER GANS' HISTORY CLASS.

THEN HOW ABOUT IN THE LOUNGE? I MEAN, YOU AND COMMANDER RIKER ARE FRIENDS. HE COULD AT LEAST HAVE DROPPED A HINT.

THAT'S RIGHT, MISTER BEN-DAVID. HE COULD HAVE-- BUT HE *DIDN'T*.

ENSIGN CRUSHER'S STATUS AS MY FRIEND HAS NOTHING TO DO WITH WHAT GOES ON IN MY CLASS.

8

OF COURSE NOT, COMMANDER. I DIDN'T MEAN TO SUGGEST THAT--

I THINK I *KNOW* WHAT YOU WERE SUGGESTING, ARI. BUT SET YOUR MIND AT EASE.

NEITHER WESLEY NOR ANYONE ELSE GETS SPECIAL TREATMENT FROM ME. THAT'S NOT THE WAY THINGS WORK ON THIS SHIP--OR IN *LIFE*, FOR THAT MATTER.

UNDERSTOOD?

SURE, COMMANDER. I WAS JUST KIDDING-- HONEST.

ALL KIDDING ASIDE, WES, I MEANT WHAT I TOLD YOUR FRIEND. NO SPECIAL TREAT- MENT JUST BECAUSE YOU AND I KNOW EACH OTHER OUTSIDE THE CLASSROOM.

LISTEN, THAT WAS ALL ARI'S IDEA. I KNOW YOU'VE GOT TO BE FAIR TO EVERYONE.

GOOD. JUST SO LONG AS YOU KNOW WHERE I STAND.

DEANNA... IS IT GOING TO BE MUCH FARTHER NOW?

NOT *TOO MUCH* FARTHER.

IS THAT A *BROOK* I HEAR?

YES, IT IS. I MODELED IT AFTER ONE IN THE WILDERNESS PARK NEAR MY HOME. YOU KNOW-- ON BETAZED.

IS THAT WHAT THIS IS? A *RECONSTRUCTION* OF THAT PLACE?

ACTUALLY, IT'S AN *AMALGAM* OF LOTS OF *DIFFERENT* PLACES. THE FLOWERS ARE FROM THE *DELTA FUEGO* SYSTEM. AND THE BIRDS ARE A RARE BREED I ONCE SAW ON *LYSANDER'S* WORLD.

IS IT MY *IMAGINATION*, OR IS THIS TRAIL GETTING *STEEPER*?

IT'S PROBABLY YOUR IMAGINATION.

10

DATA--OVER HERE!

PULL UP A CHAIR, DATA. WE NEED ANOTHER PERSPECTIVE.

ANOTHER PERSPECTIVE? ON WHAT?

O'BRIEN AND I WERE JUST COMPARING DAYDREAMS. YOU KNOW--IF YOU HAD ALL OF SPACE TO CHOOSE FROM, WHO WOULD YOU BE?

I SAID THAT IF I COULD BE ANYONE I WISHED, I'D BE MY UNCLE SEAN.

Y'SEE, UNCLE SEAN HAS A COZY LITTLE WATERING HOLE ON ALPHA NARNIA SEVEN. NOT A TERRIBLY FANCY PLACE, MIND YOU--BUT ALPHA NARNIA SEVEN HAS SOME OF THE FINEST-LOOKING WOMEN IN THE GALAXY. AND ON LADIES' NIGHT--

OKAY, WE GET THE PICTURE. AND IT DOESN'T SOUND HALF BAD.

BUT YOU NEVER MET TAMIERON THE TINKER.

THIS GUY OWNS A MOON IN THE GAMMA MERIDIEN SYSTEM. AND IT'S COVERED WITH WRECKS HE'S SALVAGED ALL OVER THE GALAXY.

IMAGINE ALL THAT HARDWARE TO PLAY WITH--AND NOTHING BUT TIME IN WHICH TO DO IT. NO DEADLINES, NO PRESSURE...

...THAT'D BE HEAVEN, AS FAR AS I'M CONCERNED.

CARE TO BREAK THE TIE, COMMANDER? OR HAVE YOU GOT YOUR OWN IDEA OF PARADISE?

I DO NOT WISH TO SEEM UNIMAGINATIVE, GENTLEMEN. BUT I HAVE LEARNED THAT THERE IS ONLY ONE PLACE FOR ME...

...AND THAT PLACE IS HERE ABOARD THE ENTERPRISE.

12

AND OF COURSE, NO DISCUSSION OF THE WAR FOR INDEPENDENCE WOULD BE COMPLETE WITHOUT REFERENCE TO ONE OF ITS MORE COLORFUL FIGURES-- THE INFAMOUS BENEDICT ARNOLD.

EARLY IN THE WAR, ARNOLD PROVED HIMSELF AS AN ABLE MILITARY LEADER. HOWEVER, HIS ABRASIVE PERSONALITY AND SHADY FINANCIAL DEALINGS MADE HIM UNPOPULAR WITH THE COLONIAL CONGRESS.

EVENTUALLY, TIRED OF WATCHING LESS CAPABLE MEN PROMOTED PAST HIM, ARNOLD BECAME BITTER AND DISILLUSIONED WITH THE COLONIAL CAUSE. IN 1780, HE STRUCK A DEAL WITH MAJOR JOHN ANDRE OF THE BRITISH ARMY--TO TURN OVER WEST POINT FOR A SMALL FORTUNE IN BRITISH CURRENCY.

ARNOLD'S PLOT WAS FOILED WHEN ANDRE WAS CAPTURED--STRICTLY THROUGH CHANCE-- AND HE WAS HANGED AS A SPY.

ARNOLD FLED TO GREAT BRITAIN, WHERE HE BECAME A VALUABLE COG IN THE BRITISH WAR MACHINE. HE RETURNED TO NORTH AMERICA AS A BRIGADIER GENERAL--

UH... SIR?

YES, MISTER CRUSHER?

WHAT ABOUT THE MONTMORENCY MONOGRAPH-- "BENEDICT ARNOLD, PATRIOT"?

13

THE... MONTMORENCY MONOGRAPH?

SIR, ISN'T MONTMORENCY PRETTY MUCH ACCEPTED NOW AS THE FINAL AUTHORITY ON BENEDICT ARNOLD?

AND MONTMORENCY STATES THAT ARNOLD WAS IN ALL LIKELIHOOD A DOUBLE AGENT-- ONE WHO NEVER INTENDED TO SELL OUT HIS COUNTRY.

ACCORDING TO MONTMORENCY, ARNOLD ARRANGED MAJOR ANDRE'S CAPTURE... AND LATER, AS A BRITISH GENERAL, SECRETLY HELPED THE COLONIAL ARMY BY SENDING CRUCIAL BITS OF INFORMATION TO GENERAL WASHINGTON.

YOU HAVE HEARD OF MONTMORENCY--HAVEN'T YOU, SIR?

TRUTH BE TOLD, MISTER CRUSHER-- NO, I HAVEN'T.

BUT THANK YOU FOR BRINGING THAT THEORY UP. I WOULDN'T HAVE WANTED THE CLASS TO MISS IT.

14

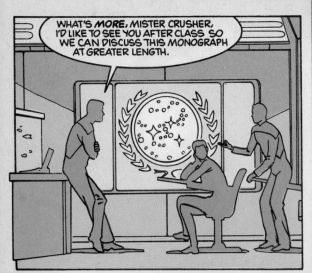

WHAT'S *MORE*, MISTER CRUSHER, I'D LIKE TO SEE YOU AFTER CLASS SO WE CAN DISCUSS THIS MONOGRAPH AT GREATER LENGTH.

UH... SURE.

NOW LET'S LOOK AT ANOTHER COLORFUL FIGURE OF THE DAY-- ONE WHOSE CHARACTER, I TRUST, HAS NOT BEEN REASSESSED IN A RECENT MONOGRAPH...

YOU'VE GOT TO BE KIDDING!

15

NOT AT ALL. IT WILL BE FUN.

JUMPING ACROSS A RAGING RIVER IS FUN?

I THOUGHT YOU SAID THIS WAS A BROOK?

IT WAS--IN THE SUMMER AND FALL. BUT IN THE SPRING, IT WAS MORE LIKE THIS--ENGORGED WITH THE MELT OFF FROM THE MOUNTAINS.

WHEN WE WERE CHILDREN, WE USED TO JUMP IT ALL THE TIME.

WHAT IS THE WORST THAT COULD HAPPEN? IF IT SEEMS THAT ONE OF US WILL NOT MAKE IT, WE WILL ABORT THE PROGRAM--AND FIND OURSELVES SAFE AND SOUND IN AN EMPTY HOLODECK.

WHY CAN'T WE DO THAT NOW? REALLY, DEANNA-- I THINK I'LL ENJOY YOUR GIFT JUST AS MUCH IF YOU JUST TELL ME ABOUT IT.

COME ON, BEVERLY. IT'S NOT AS DIFFICULT AS IT LOOKS.

JUST TAKE A RUNNING START AND--

--DO IT!

YOU SEE? NOW IT'S *YOUR* TURN!

I CAN'T BELIEVE I'M LETTING YOU TALK ME INTO THIS--INTO *ANY* OF THIS.

HERE GOES--

--NOTHING!

...MUCH TO DO HERE IN FERGUS FALLS, BUT AUNT MEGAN'S NICE ENOUGH. SHE EVEN OFFERED TO TAKE ME TO SAN FRANCISCO FOR A COUPLE OF WEEKS THIS SUMMER-- SO I CAN VISIT STARFLEET ACADEMY.

JEREMY ASTER: STARDATE 44270.1, EARTH

I'D LOVE TO SEE THE ACADEMY AND ALL, BUT...WELL, YOU SEE, THERE'S THIS GIRL AT SCHOOL THAT I KIND OF LIKE. HER NAME'S EMILY.

I THINK SHE LIKES ME BACK, TOO, BUT SHE ALSO LIKES THIS OTHER GUY. AND I'M AFRAID THAT IF I GO TO SAN FRANCISCO FOR SO LONG, THE OTHER GUY WILL GET HER.

I WISH I COULD TALK TO YOU IN PERSON ABOUT THIS, WORF. BUT SINCE I CAN'T, MAYBE YOU CAN SEND A MESSAGE BACK REAL QUICK--SO I'LL KNOW WHAT TO DO.

SEE YA. SOS JIH BATLH SOH.

RETURN TRANSMISSION

STAY, JEREMY ASTER.

AND FIGHT.

⑱

DEANNA, THIS IS *RIDICULOUS.* I'M NOT GOING TO TAKE ANOTHER STEP UNTIL YOU GIVE ME A CLUE AS TO WHAT WE'RE *DOING* HERE!

WE'RE ALMOST THERE. DON'T TELL ME YOU'RE GOING TO QUIT *NOW!*

OH, *NO.* OF COURSE NOT. WHY SHOULD I QUIT WHEN I'M HAVING *SUCH* A GOOD TIME?

AH. BEVERLY, YOU'LL BE GLAD TO KNOW THAT...

...AT LONG LAST, WE ARE HERE.

THANK GOD. I DON'T THINK I'VE GOT ANY SKIN LEFT ON MY--

--LORD, DEANNA. IT'S...

19

SOMETHING LIKE THAT. SOMETIMES IT IS EASIER TO SHOW THAN TO TELL.

I GUESS AGE IS A STATE OF MIND. BECAUSE RIGHT NOW, BRUISES AND ALL, I FEEL LIKE A TEENAGER AGAIN.

ISN'T THAT FUNNY? IT *WORKED!* I GUESS YOU KNOW YOUR BUSINESS, COUNSELOR.

FORTUNATELY, YOURS WAS NOT AN *EXTREME* CASE. FOR THOSE, I MUST RESORT TO AN ALTERNATIVE TREATMENT.

OH? AND WHAT'S THAT?

I SEE.

HAPPY BIRTHDAY, BEVERLY.

THANK YOU, DEANNA.

21

COMMANDER?

AH, MISTER CRUSHER. HAVE A SEAT.

YES, SIR.

DO YOU HAVE ANY IDEA WHY I'VE ASKED YOU TO SEE ME?

UH... I THINK SO.

I MADE YOU LOOK BAD IN FRONT OF THE CLASS. I DAMAGED YOUR CREDIBILITY.

YOU ALSO HURT ME PERSONALLY, WES. WE'RE FRIENDS. I EXPECTED TO BE TREATED LIKE ONE.

BUT... YOU SAID THAT...

AND I WAS ABSOLUTELY RIGHT.

22

IF YOU WANT, I'LL CALL IT UP FOR YOU. THAT WAY, YOU CAN READ IT AT YOUR LEISURE.

I GUESS I'LL HAVE TO LOOK UP THAT MONOGRAPH NOW. I'D HATE TO GET CAUGHT WITH MY PANTS DOWN A SECOND TIME.

THAT'S ALL RIGHT, WES. YOU'VE CONTRIBUTED ENOUGH TO MY EDUCATION FOR ONE DAY.

BESIDES-- WHOA! WHAT HAPPENED HERE?

MOM--ARE YOU ALL RIGHT? YOU LOOK LIKE YOU'VE BEEN THROUGH A KLINGON RITE OF PASSAGE!

I MAY NOT LOOK SO GOOD, WES--BUT I FEEL WONDERFUL!

THE END

"Every silver lining has a dark,
  dark cloud;
Always after sunshine comes
  the rain;
They say that after night, the
  dawn is sure to be bright;
But don't forget the night will
  come again."

--TWENTIETH CENTURY
SCHOOL RHYME

THE GIFT

JOHN de LANCIE
WRITER

GORDON
PURCELL
PENCILLER

PABLO MARCOS
INKER

BOB PINAHA
LETTERER

JULIANNA
FERRITER
COLORIST

ROBERT
GREENBERGER
EDITOR

ADDITIONAL
DIALOGUE BY
MICHAEL JAN
FRIEDMAN

BASED ON
STAR TREK:
THE NEXT
GENERATION
CREATED BY
GENE
RODDENBERRY

EXCUSE ME, SIR, BUT THE PARTY IS ABOUT TO START.

DID YOU HEAR ME, SIR?

YES, I HEARD YOU, NUMBER ONE.

I THINK YOU WOULD ENJOY IT. THE CREW HAS MADE QUITE AN EFFORT...

...ARE YOU ALL RIGHT, CAPTAIN?

YES, NUMBER ONE, I'M ALL RIGHT. I WAS THINKING ABOUT SOMETHING THAT HAPPENED A LONG, LONG TIME AGO...

I'M SORRY, WILL, BUT I DON'T FEEL MUCH LIKE A PARTY TONIGHT. YOU GO AHEAD.

THERE WERE AT LEAST FIFTY OF THEM! THE SHIELDS WERE DOWN AND THE SHIP WAS DEFENSELESS! MY PHASER WAS GONE...

FORGIVE ME FOR INTERRUPTING SIR, BUT YOU HAVE CONFUSED THE DETAILS.

2

ARE YOU QUESTIONING MY FACTS--AGAIN?

MOST RESPECTFULLY, YES.

WELL...MAYBE YOU'RE RIGHT. LET'S SAY TWENTY.

LET US SAY TWO, TO BE PRECISE. QUITE OLD AND VERY SLOW.

THAT'S IT! I'VE HAD IT WITH YOU, DATA! LET GUINAN DECIDE WHO'S RIGHT!

WELL?

QUITE FRANKLY, FOR THE SAKE OF GOOD RELATIONS, AND THE SPIRIT OF THE EVENING-- I DON'T REMEMBER!

3

VERY DIPLOMATIC.

CLAP CLAP CLAP

SPACE

HEAR YE, HEAR YE! THE SHOW IS ABOUT TO BEGIN!

OUR LITTLE STORY HERE TONIGHT, IS JUST FOR FUN AND NOT FOR FRIGHT!

THIS SPACE FOR RENT!

WE AIM TO PLEASE, THAT'S FOR SURE, WE WANT TO KEEP OUR JOBS SECURE!

SIR, YOU ARE REQUESTED ON THE BRIDGE.

WHAT'S THE PROBLEM, ENSIGN?

WE HAVE AN UNUSUALLY LARGE...MAGNETIC...FIELD WHICH HAS RIPPED THE...THE...THE...

THE WHAT?!

...I...I CAN'T SEEM TO REMEMBER, SIR...

4

...THE...THE TECHNICAL TERM HAS ESCAPED ME FOR THE MOMENT.

OUR STORY UNFOLDS ON A FAR AWAY SEA WHERE THE CAPTAIN IS PLAYING WITH THREE NYMPHI.

RIKER IS OFF, PHASER IN HAND, SLAYING DEMONS IN THIS HEATHEN LAND.

THE SEA

WE ON THE SHIP NEED ONLY BE TOLD THAT... THAT...

I THINK SHE'S FORGOTTEN HER LINES. AND NONE TOO SOON BY THE LOOKS OF IT!

HAHAHAHA

⑤

CAPTAIN, THERE'S SOMETHING WRONG!

WHAT'S THE PROBLEM?

WE'RE PICKING UP A DISTURBANCE.

SIR, SENSORS INDICATE AN IMMENSE ENERGY FIELD-- HEADED RIGHT FOR US!

RAISE THE SHIELDS.

A FURY. THAT'S THE BEST I CAN MAKE OF IT. AN EXTRAORDINARILY COMPLEX...FURY, THAT...

GO TO YELLOW ALERT, ENSIGN.

I SAID, YELLOW ALERT.

I'M SORRY, SIR, BUT I...I...DON'T REMEMBER HOW TO GIVE THE...

6

SHHZZK!

GRAB HIM! HOLD HIM DOWN!

EVERYONE OUT OF THE WAY. PUT YOUR WEAPONS ON STUN!

HUH--?

NOOOO!

9

EXCUSE THE INCONVENIENCE. BUT YOUR CAPTAIN AND I ARE HAVING A LITTLE CHIT-CHAT. DON'T GO AWAY.

BAM BAM

SIT DOWN, PICARD. TAKE A LOAD OFF YOUR MIND.

I'VE COME TO TELL YOU THAT I DON'T LIKE YOU ANY MORE. AS FAR AS I'M CONCERNED, THE HONEYMOON IS OVER.

FAVORS HAVE BEEN DONE, DEBTS COLLECTED AND NOW, THE SLATE IS CLEAN!

WHO IS THIS?

MYYYY... MY...

MYYYY...MYYYY... WHAT?! HAVING A LITTLE PROBLEM WITH THE OLD BRAIN CELLS, PICARD? YOUR MIND NOT SERVING YOU THE WAY IT SHOULD?

COME NOW, THINK HARD, SURELY YOU MUST REMEMBER.

MYY...
PARRRR...

GOOD GOD. IF I
KNEW THAT TALKING
TO A GOAT WOULD
BE THIS MUCH FUN,
I WOULD HAVE
PICKED ANOTHER
"Q"UADRUPED!

DON'T CLAUDE
AND CHRISTINE
MEAN ANYTHING
TO YOU?

MYYYYY...
PARRRENTS...

NOT ANY
MORE!

I HAVE AN ANNOUNCEMENT
TO MAKE! THE CAPTAIN AND I
HAVE A LITTLE HOME COMING
TO ATTEND. DON'T
WAIT UP!

FOSH

SKRITCH
SKRITCH

⑫

I-I MUST GET TO MY MOTHER'S HOUSE.

2332? IF- IF THAT'S THE CORRECT DATE--

--MY GOD, MY FATHER IS STILL ALIVE!

PICARD

BONJOUR, MAMA. BONJOUR, PAPA.

13

WHAT ARE YOU DOING IN OUR HOUSE? YOU HAVE NO RIGHT TO ENTER OUR HOUSE.

BUT I HAVE EVERY RIGHT, I AM YOUR SON!

WHAT? ARE YOU OUT OF YOUR MIND?

DON'T YOU RECOGNIZE ME, PAPA?

NO, I DO NOT!

JEAN LUC-- DESCEND!

THAT... MAN IS A FAKE, AN IMPOSTOR!

CHRISTINE, CALL THE GENDARME.

PAPA, THIS MAN IS ILL.

SMASH!

HAH HA

FOOSH

⑮

97

STOP. THIS IS NOTHING MORE THAN A MEAN-SPIRITED CHILD PULLING THE WINGS OFF A FLY.

AT LEAST LET ME FIGHT FOR MY LIFE. CHALLENGE ME!

WHAT DO YOU SUGGEST?

I SUGGEST YOU LET MY PARENTS CHOOSE BETWEEN US. LET THEM CHOOSE THEIR TRUE SON.

WHAT MAKES YOU THINK THEY WILL KNOW THE DIFFERENCE?

MY PARENTS WILL KNOW ME AS THEIR SON, IN SPITE OF YOU.

HOW?

OUR LIFE SHARED TOGETHER. THE REMEMBERING OF THINGS PAST...

YOU HAD BETTER BE VERY CONVINCING WITH DEAR OLD MAMA AND PAPA, BECAUSE IF YOU ARE NOT-- YOU MAY FIND YOURSELF COUSIN TO A SLUG BEFORE YOU CAN SAY, "Q'S BACK"!

SNAP!

ALL SYSTEMS ARE AGAIN FUNCTIONAL, SIR. AND THE ENERGY FIELD SEEMS TO BE GONE.

THANK YOU, WORF. NOW BEST AS I CAN MAKE OF IT, Q ABDUCTED THE CAPTAIN FOR REASONS UNKNOWN.

WE THINK HE AFFECTED THE MEMORY OF CERTAIN MEMBERS OF THE CREW--ALSO FOR REASONS UNKNOWN.

IS THERE ANYTHING WE KNOW?

AS A MATTER OF FACT, SIR, THERE IS.

WE KNOW THAT Q HAS TAKEN THE CAPTAIN TO A "HOMECOMING," AS HE PUT IT.

WHICH MEANS?

IT COULD MEAN A NUMBER OF THINGS, SIR. EITHER BACK TO THE CONTINUUM, OR TO...

EXCUSE ME, BUT I THINK THIS MAY BE OF HELP.

I THINK WHEN Q SAID "HOME," HE MAY HAVE MEANT THE CAPTAIN'S HOME-- THE CAPTAIN'S PARENTS' HOME.

KNOCK
KNOCK

YOU DON'T KNOW WHO I AM, BUT PLEASE HEAR ME OUT.

I AM CAUGHT IN A GREAT STRUGGLE. WHAT I HAVE TO LOSE ARE NOT ONLY THE MEMORIES OF MY LIFE, BUT MY LIFE ITSELF!

JEAN LUC-- DESCEND!

WHAT ARE YOU DOING IN OUR HOUSE? YOU HAVE NO RIGHT TO ENTER OUR HOUSE!

⑳

WHAT YOU ARE ABOUT TO HEAR WILL SOUND EXTRAORDINARY TO YOU...

CHRISTINE, CALL THE GENDARMES!

NO, FATHER. TAKE PITY ON THIS MAN. LET'S HEAR HIS STORY...

BUT DATA... THE CAPTAIN'S PARENTS' HOME IS ON EARTH! THAT'S ON THE OTHER SIDE OF FEDERATION SPACE!

WHAT'S MORE, THEY NO LONGER LIVE IN THIS PLACE. THE CAPTAIN'S FATHER PASSED AWAY SOME YEARS AGO--AND HIS MOTHER MOVED SHORTLY THEREAFTER. OR AT LEAST THAT'S WHAT THE CAPTAIN TOLD ME.

NONETHELESS, Q MADE MENTION OF A HOMECOMING. AND SINCE WE DO NOT KNOW THE EXTENT OF HIS POWERS, WE CANNOT RULE OUT--

TIME TRAVEL! TO THE PARIS OF THE CAPTAIN'S BOYHOOD!

21

DO YOU REALIZE WHAT THAT MEANS? WHAT KIND OF DANGER WE MAY BE IN? IF Q IS ABLE TO GO BACK IN TIME...THEN THEORETICALLY, HE'S CAPABLE OF CHANGING THE COURSE OF EVENTS!

CHANGING THEM? TO WHAT EXTENT?

ALL WE CAN DO IS SPECULATE, COUNSELOR. BUT I'D SAY THAT DEPENDS ON WHAT KIND OF STRINGS HE PULLS!

YOU SAVE A POOR PARISIAN MOUSE FROM AN ALLEYCAT, IT PROBABLY DOESN'T MEAN MUCH. NEITHER MICE NOR ALLEYCATS HAVE HAD MAJOR IMPACTS ON RECENT HISTORY.

BUT START A FIRE IN SOME OLD PARISIAN HOTEL, AND WHO KNOWS? MAYBE ONE OF THE PEOPLE WHO BUILT MY VISOR DOESN'T LIVE TO MAKE HIS CONTRIBUTION AND I NEVER MAKE IT OUT INTO SPACE.

OR WORSE--SUPPOSE A TREATY WERE NEVER SIGNED WITH THE KLINGONS AND THE FEDERATION SUDDENLY FOUND ITSELF AT WAR? AS YOU CAN SEE, THE POSSIBILITIES ARE ENDLESS.

BUT IF Q WERE GOING TO ALTER HISTORY--RESHAPE THE PRESENT-- WOULDN'T IT HAVE HAPPENED ALREADY? WOULDN'T WE HAVE FELT THE CHANGES?

THAT WOULD MAKE SENSE, WOULDN'T IT? SO MAYBE WE'RE SAFE-- FOR NOW.

BUT THAT IS HARDLY A GUARANTEE. WE ARE IN CONSTANT PERIL--JUST AS SURELY AS IF WE WERE SURROUNDED BY ENEMY WARSHIPS.

I'D TAKE THE ENEMY WARSHIPS ANY DAY, LIEUTENANT. IN FACT, I'D TAKE ANYTHING OVER THIS.

22

I HAD FORGOTTEN ALL ABOUT THAT. HOW WOULD YOU KNOW ABOUT THAT?

FATHER, IT'S VERY SIMPLE. WHEN WE SWAM TO SHORE, A MAN WAS STANDING ON THE BEACH. HE TOOK US TO HIS HOUSE, REMEMBER?

REMEMBER, SON: WE MADE IT, WE CAN FIX IT.

YES...?

HE HAD A LITTLE BOY, ABOUT MY AGE. THIS MAN, STANDING BEFORE US, COULD BE THAT CHILD, EVEN THOUGH HE CLAIMS TO BE YOUR SON.

BUT HOW WOULD I HAVE KNOWN ABOUT THE BOAT HOOK?!

BECAUSE I TOLD EVERYBODY AT SCHOOL ABOUT IT THE NEXT DAY!

OF COURSE, THAT'S RIGHT! EVERYONE IN TOWN KNEW ABOUT OUR SAILING MISHAP. AND EVERYONE THOUGHT IT WAS QUITE FUNNY.

AND DON'T FORGET, FATHER, YOU SAVED THE COMPASS YOU HAD GIVEN ME FOR MY BIRTHDAY, BY PUTTING IT AROUND YOUR NECK AS WE SWAM TO SHORE.

YOU DIDN'T REMEMBER THAT, DID YOU-- MR. WHATEVER YOUR NAME IS?

THAT'S RIGHT, JEAN LUC! WELL, YOUNG MAN, WHAT DO YOU HAVE TO SAY NOW?

I SENSE GREAT ANGER, COMMANDER. GREAT FRUSTRATION.

AND PERHAPS NOT JUST FROM THE SITUATION AT HAND.

YOU DON'T KNOW WHAT IT'S LIKE, DEANNA--TO BE TOYED WITH, THE WAY Q IS PROBABLY TOYING WITH THE CAPTAIN RIGHT NOW.

YOU'RE REFERRING TO THE TIME Q GRANTED YOU POWERS EQUAL TO HIS?

NOT EQUAL, DEANNA. MAYBE I THOUGHT SO AT THE TIME, BUT I KNOW DIFFERENTLY NOW.

I WAS JUST POWERFUL ENOUGH TO PROVIDE SOME ENTERTAINMENT FOR HIM.

YOU REMEMBER WHEN Q BROUGHT US FACE TO FACE WITH THE BORG? AND HOW THE CAPTAIN GOT US OUT OF IT BY SIMPLY ADMITTING WE WERE OVERMATCHED?

HOW COULD I FORGET?

IF IT WAS ME, COUNSELOR, I DON'T THINK I WOULD HAVE THOUGHT OF SUCH A SIMPLE SOLUTION. I MIGHT HAVE BEEN TOO BUSY TRYING TO WRING Q'S NECK!

GIVE YOURSELF A LITTLE MORE CREDIT, COMMANDER. I'VE NOTICED THAT YOU KEEP A COOL HEAD AS WELL AS ANYONE--LIKE WITH Q'S LAST VISIT, WHEN HE WAS HUMAN. ANNOYINGLY HUMAN.

25

WELL, GO ON. WHAT *REMEMBRANCE* DO YOU PLAN TO ENTERTAIN US WITH *NEXT?* IT HAD BETTER BE GOOD.

SNAP!

MY "PARENTS" ARE LOSING PATIENCE. AND SO AM I...

FATHER, DO YOU REMEMBER THE TIME I GOT INTO A FIGHT AT SCHOOL? RATHER THAN STOP THE FIGHT, YOU CHOSE TO SEE WHO WOULD WIN. DO YOU REMEMBER?

YES, I THINK SO...

IT WAS A SORT OF "LESSON..."

COME NOW, IS THIS THE *BEST* YOU CAN DO?! SAILBOAT RIDES AND SCHOOL-YARD BRAWLS? SOMETHING THAT *EVERY* CHILD HAS EXPERIENCED AND EVERY PARENT HAS FORGOTTEN.

YOU SAY YOU ARE FIGHTING FOR YOUR LIFE-- LET'S SEE IT, BE *CREATIVE!*

DAMN.

I WISH I COULD HAVE BEEN UP ON THE BRIDGE, WESLEY. I MIGHT HAVE BEEN ABLE TO STOP HIM.

STOP Q? HOW?

26

THERE'S TALK UP ON THE BRIDGE THAT THE CAPTAIN MAY NOT COME BACK. THAT Q MAY BE BITTER ENOUGH ABOUT HIS FALL FROM GRACE TO TOY WITH THE CAPTAIN FOREVER.

I HAVE MY WAYS, WES. BUT Q AND I HAVE... AN UNDERSTANDING. I WON'T--CAN'T--INTERFERE. SORRY.

I'D LIKE TO TELL YOU NOT TO WORRY, WES. I REALLY WOULD.

BUT I CAN'T--NOT THIS TIME. OUR FRIENDS ON THE BRIDGE MIGHT BE RIGHT.

Q HAS BEEN DISGRACED IN FRONT OF HIS PEERS IN THE CONTINUUM. AND IN HIS EYES, IT'S OUR CAPTAIN WHO WAS RESPONSIBLE FOR IT--AND WHO HELPED HIM GET BACK IN THE CONTINUUM. Q DOES NOT LIKE TO OWE A DEBT.

THERE ARE NO BOUNDS TO Q'S POTENTIAL FOR PETTINESS--FOR CRUELTY. UNDER THE CIRCUMSTANCES, THERE'S NOTHING I WOULDN'T PUT PAST HIM.

27

THIS IS ENOUGH. I AM CALLING THE POLICE MYSELF.

NO, FATHER, LET HIM SAY HIS FULL.

"THE CASTLES OF SPAIN ARE ALL IN A ROW...

"...WHEN MY TOE IS HURT WE HAVE TO GO...

"...THE MONSTERS ARE NEAR BUT I DON'T CARE...

"...WHEN YOU HOLD ME TIGHT, THEY'RE EASY TO SCARE."

I REMEMBER! IT'S THE CODE! THE CODE! WHEN YOU WERE LITTLE WE HAD A CODE! REMEMBER, MAMA?

YES, YES!

"THE TROUBLE WITH SNAILS IS THAT THEY'RE SLOW..."

MEANT... "WE ALL HAD TO...HURRY UP." RIGHT?

THAT'S RIGHT, YOU REMEMBERED! NOW WHAT ABOUT THIS ONE, "YOU HAVE TO BE CAREFUL WITH DOGS THAT BARK... YOU...YOU..."

"...CAN'T ALWAYS SEE THEM IN THE DARK!"

THAT WAS OUR CODE MESSAGE FOR... "BE CAREFUL WALKING HOME FROM SCHOOL."

OR WHAT ABOUT THIS ONE-- "YOU'RE THE CAPTAIN NOW, MY BOY..."

GO ON-- COMPLETE IT!

WHAT'S THE MATTER... LOST YOUR TONGUE?

㉙

111

I CAN'T...

FATHER, YOU MUST REMEMBER. IT IS WHAT YOU USED TO TELL ME JUST BEFORE LEAVING THE HOUSE.

WHY SO GLUM?

CAT GOT YOUR TONGUE? THAT WAS OUR CODE WORD FOR, "TAKE CARE OF YOUR LITTLE BROTHER." YOU SAID IT TO ME THE DAY HE FELL INTO THE WELL AND DIED...

GO ON, COMPLETE THE STORY, IF YOU KNOW SO MUCH ABOUT MY FAMILY...

I....I... CAN'T...

WELL, I CAN!

30

FATHER AND MOTHER WERE GOING TO VISIT AUNT YVONNE. IT WAS A BEAUTIFUL DAY AND CLAUDE AND I WERE PLAYING IN THE YARD. IT WAS MY JOB TO LOOK AFTER HIM

"...I WENT INSIDE TO WORK ON MY MODEL SHIPS. HE WANTED TO HELP ME, BUT I TOLD HIM NO. AND TO GET HIM OUT OF MY HAIR, I GAVE HIM AN OLD MODEL BOAT AND SENT HIM OUTSIDE.

"CLAUDE MUST HAVE CLIMBED THE FENCE AND CROSSED THE ROAD, BECAUSE WHEN I THOUGHT TO LOOK FOR HIM, HE WAS NOT IN THE YARD."

FOR HOURS I SEARCHED...

...DO YOU CARE TO CONTINUE?

DON'T DO THIS... PLEASE...

"FINALLY, LATE THAT NIGHT, ONE OF THE TOWNSPEOPLE SHINED A LIGHT DOWN A SMALL ABANDONED WELL.

"THERE WAS MY BROTHER. HIS CLOTHES TORN, BLOOD AROUND HIS FACE AND HIS NECK TWISTED...

STOP, STOP, YOU WIN!!!

...HIS NECK TWISTED COMPLETELY AROUND! WHEN THEY CARRIED HIM OUT HE WAS STILL CLUTCHING THE MODEL BOAT I HAD GIVEN HIM.

31

AND HERE IT IS. WELL, NOW WHO REMEMBERS BEST?

I THINK IT IS TIME TO CALL THE GENDARMES.

I DON'T KNOW WHO YOU ARE, BUT MY HEART TELLS ME YOU ARE NOT MY SON. MY SON WOULD NOT PUT US THROUGH THIS ANGUISH AGAIN.

SHALL I SET A COURSE, COMMANDER?

NO, DATA. WE'RE GOING TO STAY RIGHT WHERE WE ARE--SO WHEN Q RETURNS OUR CAPTAIN, HE'LL KNOW WHERE TO FIND US.

SIR--WHAT IF HE RETURNS, BUT WITHOUT THE CAPTAIN? AND DECIDES TO TAKE HIS ANGER OUT ON THE REST OF US?

32

THEN RUNNING WON'T HELP US, LIEUTENANT. WE BOTH KNOW THAT Q CAN TRACK US DOWN NO MATTER WHERE WE ARE.

"FIRST OFFICER'S PERSONAL LOG, SUPPLEMENTAL. I HAVE DECIDED TO MAINTAIN OUR POSITION, IN THE HOPE THAT CAPTAIN PICARD CAN OUTWIT Q, AS HE'S DONE IN THE PAST.

"BUT, I MUST ADMIT, IF ONLY TO MYSELF, THE POSSIBILITY THAT THE CAPTAIN WILL FINALLY RUN OUT OF WAYS TO DEAL WITH THIS SUPER-BEING.

"AND EVEN IF HE DOES MANAGE TO OUTMANEUVER HIS ADVERSARY ONCE AGAIN...WILL Q ABIDE BY THE RULES OF WHATEVER GAME HE'S INVENTED? OR WILL HE GIVE IN TO A WHIM--AND MAKE THE CAPTAIN PAY THE PRICE?"

33

I WON!

THE GAME IS UP! MY PARENTS CHOSE. THEY SAW THROUGH YOU. AND NOW, I MAKE THE DEMANDS!

MY PARENTS ARE TO HAVE NO MEMORY OF THIS, DO YOU HEAR? THE SLATE IS TO BE WIPED CLEAN!

I DON'T UNDERSTAND. I WAS ACCURATE IN EVERY DETAIL. I REMEMBERED EVERYTHING. AND YET, THEY STILL CHOSE YOU.

NEED I SPELL IT OUT, Q? SEND ME BACK NOW!

I HAVE MUCH TO LEARN. YOU HAVE PROVEN THAT. AS A GESTURE, ALLOW ME TO CHANGE THINGS, EVER SO SLIGHTLY... LET ME GIVE YOU A GIFT...

...LET ME GIVE YOU BACK YOUR BROTHER!

SURELY, THIS IS NOT SOMETHING YOU NEED TO PONDER? A BROTHER RETURNS. A FAMILY SPARED? WHAT MORE COULD ONE HOPE FOR? AFTER ALL, IT IS THE LEAST I CAN DO. WELL...?

I...I...

34

...I... ACCEPT.

MISTER WORF--ANY SIGN OF ANYTHING UNUSUAL? ANOTHER FIREBALL, MAYBE?

OR SOMETHING ELSE THAT MIGHT REPRESENT ONE OF Q'S DRAMATIC ENTRANCES?

NO, SIR. NO SIGN OF--

GOOD! I'M SURE YOU WILL NOT REGRET IT.

--THE ENEMY.

GOOD. DON'T FORGET-- THE ENTERPRISE HAS BEEN GIVEN THE HONOR OF WATCHING THE ARMADA'S FLANK.

WE CAN'T RELAX OUR VIGILANCE FOR EVEN A MOMENT.

I DID IT FOR MY PARENTS.

OF COURSE YOU DID, PICARD! AND I DID IT FOR YOU! YOU SEE, MY GIFT HAS YET TO COME...

HONOR, MY FOOT! WHEN I SIGNED UP FOR STARFLEET, THINGS WERE A DAMNED SIGHT DIFFERENT!

35

YOU'VE TRICKED ME?!

BACK THEN, THIS WASN'T A MILITARY ORGANIZATION. IT WAS DEDICATED TO EXPLORATION, TO THE EXPANSION OF KNOWLEDGE...

...TO PEACE.

OF COURSE, THAT WAS BEFORE THE LEADER TOOK OVER. BEFORE HE REMOLDED STARFLEET POLICY TO FIT HIS IDEAS AND IDEALS.

WOULD I DO THAT...?

CAPTAIN--

--CAPTAIN RIKER! ARE YOU GUARDING OUR FLANK--OR DAYDREAMING?!

36

UNFORTUNATELY, OUR CHANCES FOR ESCAPE ARE NOT VERY GOOD. WE CANNOT SIMPLY OUTRUN OUR PURSUERS, AS WE HAVE DONE SO OFTEN IN THE PAST.

HOWEVER, I CAN TRY TO MINIMIZE OUR EXPOSURE TO ENEMY FIRE--IN THE HOPE THAT AN OPPORTUNITY WILL PRESENT ITSELF.

SUSTAINING A NUMBER OF DIRECT HITS! LOSING SHIELDS, SIR!

RETURN FIRE, WORF! PHOTON TORPEDOES!

"TORPEDO LAUNCHERS DISABLED!"

"DAMAGE REPORTS COMING IN NOW! THE HULL IS STILL INTACT, BUT ITS SURFACE TEMPERATURE IS CLIMBING RAPIDLY!"

CAPTAIN--WHAT IF WE WERE TO DROP OUT OF WARP RATHER SUDDENLY? WE MIGHT LOSE THESE JOKERS--AND EVEN IF WE DON'T, WE'LL AT LEAST BE ABLE TO USE OUR PHASERS.

GOOD IDEA, DATA-- CUT TO IMPULSE POWER-- NOW!

THE ENEMY WAS PREPARED! THE OTHER SHIPS ARE DROPPING TO IMPULSE POWER AS WELL!

PHASER BANKS DESTROYED! WE'RE HELPLESS, CAPTAIN!

SO MUCH FOR THAT IDEA!

RECEIVING A TRANSMISSION FROM THE ENEMY FLAGSHIP, SIR.

AND WE ALL KNOW WHO'S ON THAT SHIP. ON VISUAL, WORF.

37

WELL, WELL. IF IT ISN'T OUR FRIEND THE REBEL--THE TRAITOR!

I'D SAY IT'S YOU WHO IS THE TRAITOR! YOU'RE THE ONE WHO HAS PERVERTED THE IDEALS OF THE FEDERATION...TURNED STARFLEET INTO A TOOL FOR THE SUBJUGATION AND OPPRESSION OF NON-HUMAN RACES!

ONLY THE STRONG SURVIVE, RIKER. THAT ISN'T MY IDEA--IT'S MOTHER NATURE'S!

YOU'RE A GRADUATE OF STARFLEET ACADEMY. YOUR EDUCATION SHOULD HAVE COVERED SUCH TOPICS.

IT DID. AND FOR A WHILE, I FELL FOR IT--AS YOU WELL KNOW. BUT WHEN YOU RAVAGED VULCAN... DECIMATED THE BETAZOIDS... I CAME TO MY SENSES.

38

120

SO YOU MUTINIED--TOOK OVER THE SHIP YOU WERE SERVING ON. AND GATHERED OTHER TRAITORS TO YOUR BANNER...MEMBERS OF THE FEEBLE-MINDED MINORITY THAT DOES NOT HAVE THE VISION TO SEE THE RIGHTNESS OF MY SACRED CRUSADE.

WE PREFER TO THINK THAT WE *LIBERATED* THE *ENTERPRISE.* JUST AS WE'VE TRIED TO LIBERATE THE BENZITES AND THE ANDORIANS AND THE OTHER RACES YOU'VE ENSLAVED!

YOU REMIND ME OF SOMEONE, RIKER. SOMEONE I KNEW A LONG TIME AGO.

BUT THAT DOESN'T MATTER NOW. NOTHING MATTERS--EXCEPT THE FACT THAT I'VE FINALLY GOT YOU WHERE I WANT YOU!

"YOU HAVE EXACTLY FIVE MINUTES TO LOWER YOUR REMAINING SHIELDS AND SURRENDER YOURSELVES. IF YOU DO NOT COMPLY, I WILL *DESTROY* THE ENTERPRISE!"

THE *ENTERPRISE* IS A VALUABLE COMMODITY, RESPLENDENT ONE. IT WOULD BE A SHAME TO HAVE TO DESTROY IT.

YET, THAT IS *JUST* WHAT WE WILL HAVE TO DO, ADMIRAL LANZA. I KNOW THIS RIKER--HE WILL NOT SURRENDER. NOT AT ANY COST.

THE *REAL* PITY WILL BE THE LOSS OF THE KLINGON--WORF. I COULD HAVE USED HIM.

USED HIM, REVERED LEADER? TOWARD WHAT END?

39

ONCE WE HAVE DESTROYED THE REBELS, WE WILL NEED TO FIND A NEW ENEMY. AND OUR ALLIES, THE KLINGONS, WILL SERVE AS WELL AS ANY OTHER.

I WONDERED WHERE YOU WOULD LOOK FOR YOUR NEXT CHALLENGE, REVERED ONE.

IT IS THE NATURE OF A CONQUEROR TO CONQUER, ADMIRAL. DID CAESAR REST ON HIS LAURELS AFTER HE VANQUISHED THE GAULS? WAS HITLER SATISFIED WITH POLAND AND CZECHOSLOVAKIA?

WE ARE BECOMING STRONGER EVERY DAY. SOON, WE WILL BE STRONG ENOUGH TO CONFRONT THE ROMULANS--AND CONQUER THEM AS EASILY AS WE'VE CONQUERED RIKER!

THE ALLOTTED TIME IS UP, REVERED ONE. SHALL I DESTROY THE ENTERPRISE?

BY ALL MEANS, LIEUTENANT. MAKE IT SO!

FOR THE GLORY OF YOUR LEADER, THE GREAT AND TERRIBLE CLAUDE PICARD!

40

LIKE WHAT YOU SEE?

THAT IS NOT MY BROTHER!

HOW WOULD YOU KNOW? THE LAST TIME YOU SAW HIM HE WAS SIX YEARS OLD!

I NOW GIVE YOU THE GIFT OF FORESIGHT, HINDSIGHT AND ALLSIGHT...

...BUCKLE UP, PICARD. WE HAVE A LITTLE TRAVELING TO DO!

···FOOSH···

DON'T BE INSULTED BY THIS RATHER...GROTESQUE TRANSFORMATION. BUT I JUST LOVE THAT EXPRESSION YOU HUMANS HAVE-- "A FLY ON THE WALL."

WHERE IS HE?

HE'S NOT IN HIS ROOM.

WHERE COULD HE BE?

YOU SHOULDN'T HAVE TAKEN HIS BANNERS AWAY.

OH, NOW IT'S MY FAULT! I SHOULD SAY NOTHING WHEN HE PAINTS THOSE OBSCENE SLOGANS IN OUR HOME...?

OF COURSE NOT, BUT YOU KNOW THE WAY HE IS...SO... IMPRESSIONABLE.

WHAT HAS THE WORLD COME TO? HE SITS AT THE TABLE, LISTENING, JUDGING EVERYTHING WE SAY. I CAN'T EVEN TRUST MY OWN SON!

WATCH YOUR TONGUE. TIMES ARE DIFFICULT ENOUGH. NO WONDER THE BOY'S CONFUSED.

HE'S NOT CONFUSED, HE'S VENGEFUL.

BE QUIET, HE'S HERE.

WHERE HAVE YOU BEEN?!

I WAS AT THE STORE.

DO YOU THINK HE IS TELLING THE TRUTH...?

"AS YOU CAN SEE, YOUR BROTHER REALLY ENJOYS ALL THIS--"

--THE BULLYING, THE INTIMIDATING--

ZAP!

--HE'S TAKEN TO IT AS A "DUCK TAKES TO WATER."

FORGIVE THE PUN.

COME ON, PICARD...

43

...THE BEST IS YET TO BE...

YOU ARE A RISING YOUNG STAR IN OUR ORGANIZATION AND WE NOW HAVE A JOB FOR YOU TO DO.

THINK OF IT AS AN INITIATION, WHICH, IF WELL EXECUTED, WILL BE AMPLY REWARDED.

AS YOU'RE AWARE, THE POLITICAL SITUATION IS RIPE FOR THE PICKING. THE NATION NEEDS A SCAPEGOAT.

ORPHANAGE

COME CLOSER, YOUNG MAN, AND LET ME ENCOURAGE YOU TO ACTS OF GREATNESS...

44

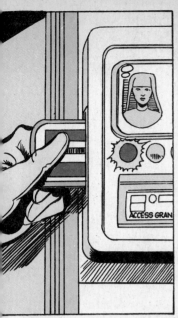

ACCESS GRANTED

I'M SORRY, PICARD, BUT IT IS THE ONLY ANIMAL I COULD THINK OF. THE ONLY ANIMAL THAT WOULD VOLUNTEER...

I CAN'T JUST WATCH...

I AGREE, THIS IS MONSTROUS... BUT, LOOK...

CLAUDE! ARE YOU OUT OF YOUR MIND?!

JEAN LUC!

OOOF!

45

I CAN'T.

BUT YOU MUST!

ALL RIGHT--

PROCEED.

WHOOSH!

⑤

133

EXCUSE ME, SIR, BUT THE PARTY IS ABOUT TO START.

DID YOU HEAR ME, SIR?

YES, I HEARD YOU, NUMBER ONE.

I THINK YOU WOULD ENJOY IT. THE CREW HAS MADE QUITE AN EFFORT...

...ARE YOU ALL RIGHT, CAPTAIN?

YES, NUMBER ONE, I'M ALL RIGHT.

I WAS THINKING ABOUT SOMETHING THAT HAPPENED A LONG, LONG TIME AGO...

...AND YOU KNOW, WILL, I WOULD LOVE TO COME TO THE PARTY!

THAT IS THE END OF THE TRANSMISSION.

I HAVE THE MARCO POLO'S COORDINATES. THEY CORRESPOND WITH THE BETA MARADA SYSTEM-- WELL BEYOND THE LIMITS OF FEDERATION TERRITORY.

AS ONE MIGHT EXPECT FROM A DEEP SPACE EXPLORATION VESSEL.

AT WARP 9.2, WE COULD BE THERE IN 1.9 DAYS, SIR.

MISTER FARMER-- PLOT A COURSE FOR BETA MARADA AT WARP 9.2.

WILL...

WHAT IS IT, COUNSELOR?

IT'S ALL RIGHT, DEANNA.

I...ER...

COUNSELOR TROI SENSED MY CONCERN FOR THE MARCO POLO, SIR-- A CONCERN WHICH IS MAGNIFIED BY THE FACT THAT I *KNOW* CAPTAIN HALK.

IN FACT, I KNOW HER QUITE WELL.

I UNDERSTAND, NUMBER ONE. REST ASSURED, WE WILL DO EVERYTHING IN OUR POWER TO ASSIST THE MARCO POLO.

"COURSE PLOTTED, MISTER FARMER?"

NCC-1701-D

"AYE, CAPTAIN."

"THEN BY ALL MEANS, ENGAGE."

COMMANDER-- I WANT YOU TO FIND OUT EVERYTHING YOU CAN ABOUT THE BETA MARADA SYSTEM. I'LL WANT TO BE BRIEFED BEFORE WE ARRIVE.

IT WOULD HAVE BEEN SIMPLER TO ASK DATA.

OF COURSE, SIR.

ABSOLUTELY, COUNSELOR...

"...THAT IS, IF INFORMATION HAD BEEN MY SOLE PURPOSE IN MAKING THE REQUEST. YOU ARE NOT THE *ONLY* ONE ON THIS SHIP WHO CAN *EMPATHIZE*, AFTER ALL."

4

MICHAEL JAN FRIEDMAN · WRITER

MATT HALEY · PENCILLER

CARLOS GARZON · INKER

BOB PINAHA · LETTERER

JULIANNA FERRITER · COLORIST

ROBERT GREENBERGER · EDITOR

BASED ON STAR TREK: THE NEXT GENERATION
CREATED BY GENE RODDENBERRY

COME ON, YOU STICK-IN-THE-MUD! I'M GETTING TIRED OF SKATING ALONE!

WILL!

LYRINDA! DON'T MOVE-- I'M COMING!

WHAT THE--? IT'S NOT BROKEN.

I GUESS IT'S NOT. MY MISTAKE.

"CAPTAIN'S LOG, STARDATE 44612.3: THE COORDINATES FROM WHICH THE DISTRESS CALL WAS SENT ARE NOW ONLY MINUTES AWAY.

"COMMANDER RIKER HAS NOT DISCUSSED HIS FEELINGS WITH ME, NOR HAVE I SOLICITED THEM. HOWEVER, *ONE* THING IS CLEAR ENOUGH--

"--HE IS NOT OPTIMISTIC ABOUT THE FATE OF THE MARCO POLO. AFTER ALL, SHE WAS ALREADY AT A TERRIBLE DISADVANTAGE WHEN HER CAPTAIN SENT OUT THAT DISTRESS CALL.

"THE SECOND ATTACK COULD VERY WELL HAVE TURNED THE SHIP INTO SPACE DEBRIS.

"THUS FAR, COMMANDER RIKER HAS NOT LET HIS PERSONAL PREOCCUPATION INTERFERE WITH HIS WORK. NOR DO I EXPECT THAT HE WILL--HE IS TOO MUCH THE CONSUMMATE PROFESSIONAL.

"HOWEVER, HIS FEELINGS FOR CAPTAIN HALK SEEM TO RUN QUITE DEEP-- AND EVEN PROFESSIONALS MAY FALTER."

THE HOURS PASS SLOWLY-- FOR ME AS WELL AS FOR HIM.

NAME: HALK, LYRINDA

RANK: CAPTAIN

CURRENT ASSIGNMENT:

U.S.S. MARCO POLO —

CHALLENGER CLASS

DEEP-SPACE EXPLORER

PART OF ME IS DOING MY JOB, LEARNING CAPTAIN HALK'S PERSONAL HISTORY--SO THAT I WILL BE BETTER PREPARED TO INTERPRET HER EMOTIONS WHEN I ENCOUNTER THEM.

THAT PART OF ME IS ALOOF, DETACHED--AS A SHIP'S COUNSELOR SHOULD BE.

BUT THE OTHER PART CAN'T HELP BUT BE WITH WILL ON THE BRIDGE.

PERSONAL HISTORY:

BORN AND RAISED IN VALDEZ, ALASKA. FATHER WAS KILLED IN FISSION PLANT ACCIDENT WHEN SUBJECT WAS TWELVE YEARS OLD.

AND THE MORE I LEARN ABOUT CAPTAIN HALK, THE DEEPER I AM DRAWN INTO HIS PAIN--

--THE MORE TERRIBLE IT SEEMS TO LOSE HER--

HISTORY CONTINUES:

GRADUATED FROM STARFLEET ACADEMY WITH HONORS. SERVED WITH DISTINCTION AS ENSIGN ABOARD U.S.S. TRIESTE.

--THOUGH I HAVE NEVER EVEN MET HER.

13

HAIL THE UNIDENTIFIED VESSELS, MISTER WORF. LET US SEE IF OUR LUCK IS ANY BETTER THAN CAPTAIN HALK'S.

AYE, SIR.

NO RESPONSE, CAPTAIN. THEY ARE NOT ANSWERING.

AND I BELIEVE I KNOW WHY. THERE IS NO ONE ON THOSE SHIPS!

BUT HOW CAN THAT BE? SOMEONE FIRED ON THE MARCO POLO!

IF I MAY SPECULATE, SIR...

BY ALL MEANS, DATA.

PERHAPS THOSE SHIPS ARE OPERATED BY ROBOT MECHANISMS, RATHER THAN BIOLOGICAL ENTITIES.

THAT WOULD EXPLAIN THE SENSOR READINGS-- *AND* THE LACK OF A RESPONSE TO OUR COMMUNICATION.

PERHAPS THEIR SENSORS WERE DAMAGED TOO SOON. REMEMBER-- THEY WERE ASSAULTED *BEFORE* THEY HAD A CHANCE TO DEFEND THEMSELVES!

BUT WHY DIDN'T THE MARCO POLO KNOW THIS?

NUMBER ONE-- ANY IDEA WHO MAY HAVE MADE THESE SHIPS? AND WHY?

AS FAR AS I CAN TELL, SIR, THERE'S ONLY ONE RACE THAT MIGHT HAVE INHABITED THIS SECTOR-- A PEOPLE CALLED THE DARZUN.

THE DARZUN? I AM NOT FAMILIAR WITH THEM.

WE'VE NEVER ACTUALLY MET THEM-- ONLY SEEN THEIR WORKS. EIGHTY YEARS AGO, FOR INSTANCE, AN EXPEDITION TO *FAR PEL SEVEN* TURNED UP AN ENTIRE DARZUN CITY.

16

APPARENTLY, THERE ARE A NUMBER OF SIMILARITIES. ONE *MIGHT* CONCLUDE THAT THE VESSELS ON THE VIEW-SCREEN ARE OF DARZUN ORIGIN.

CAPTAIN--WE ARE WITHIN PHASER RANGE.

THANK YOU, LIEUTENANT. SHIELDS UP.

NUMBER ONE--ORGANIZE AN AWAY TEAM. WE'VE GOT TO HELP THOSE PEOPLE ON THE MARCO POLO.

I THOUGHT YOU'D NEVER ASK, SIR.

YOU'RE WITH *ME*, MISTER WORF. MISTER LAFORGE, DOCTOR CRUSHER--REPORT TO TRANSPORTER ROOM ONE.

I KNOW, COUNSELOR. *PERSONAL INVOLVEMENT.* NORMALLY, IT DOES NOT ENCOURAGE TRUST.

BUT IN *HIS* CASE, I THINK HE'S *EARNED* IT.

18

LOOKS LIKE WE'VE GOT OUR WORK CUT OUT FOR US.

LAFORGE--WORF--SECURE ALL SYSTEMS. SEE WHAT WE CAN SALVAGE. DOCTOR CRUSHER-- NURSE BOND--FIND THE WORST CASES AND BEAM THEM OVER TO SICKBAY.

19

LYRINDA...?

...WILL...?

MY GOD, LYRINDA-- LOOK AT YOU.

...I'M OKAY... SEE TO...THE OTHERS...

SETTLE DOWN. WE'RE HERE NOW. EVERYTHING IS GOING TO BE ALL RIGHT.

...DAMN IT, WILL...

...YOU CALL THIS...ALL RIGHT...?

20

DAMN! WHAT A MESS!

THE CORE APPEARS UNDAMAGED.

≡KOFF!≡ THEN IT'S THE *EXCEPTION* AROUND HERE!

THERE'S NO POWER TO THE WARP FIELD GENERATORS. MUST BE A TRANSFER TUNNEL OFF-LINE SOMEWHERE--MAYBE SEVERAL.

UNFORTUNATELY, THE DIAGNOSTICS AREN'T ALL WORKING RIGHT. WE'RE GOING TO NEED TO GET INTO THE SUPPORT CONDUITS OURSELVES-- TO FIND THE GUILTY PARTIES AND GET 'EM WORKING AGAIN.

IF WE'RE LUCKY, THE PLASMA WON'T BACK UP IN THE MEANTIME AND SHUT EVERYTHING DOWN. THEN WE'D *REALLY* BE IN TROUBLE.

COMING, WORF?

AYE, SIR.

CHIEF O'BRIEN?

READY WHEN YOU ARE, DOCTOR.

SIX TO BEAM OVER. ENERGIZE.

THIS MAN COULD USE A RIDE TO THE *ENTERPRISE*, DOCTOR.

HE'LL HAVE TO WAIT HIS TURN.

INTERNAL INJURIES TAKE PRECEDENCE OVER BROKEN BONES. AND LORD KNOWS, THERE ARE ENOUGH INTERNAL INJURIES HERE TO KEEP US BUSY IN SICKBAY FOR A MONTH.

IT'S ALL RIGHT. I CAN WAIT.

THANKS FOR SAYING SO, CREWMAN...

...CAPTAIN HALK'S NEXT ON THE SCHEDULE, COMMANDER.

NO... TAKE OTHERS FIRST...

22

DAMN!

LEUNG-- ESTIMATED TIME UNTIL WE GET HER OUT OF THERE.

SEVENTEEN MINUTES, SIR, AT OUR PRESENT RATE OF PROGRESS.

NOT GOOD ENOUGH. WE'RE GOING TO EXCEED THE TIME ALLOTMENT.

I'LL TRY TO WORK FASTER, CAPTAIN.

TRANSPORTER ROOM!

DO YOUR BEST, MISTER LEUNG.

EPSTEIN

162

ALERT

CAPTAIN--THE TRANSPORTER HAS BEEN ACTIVATED!

WHAT?!

THERE'S SOMEONE AT THE HELM OF THE CASPIAN, SIR. SENSORS INDICATE ONE LIFE-FORM--HUMAN.

YOU WILL FIND THAT THAT IS CADET HALK, "CAPTAIN" RIKER. SHE LEFT YOUR BRIDGE A FEW MOMENTS AGO.

"AND I MUST SAY--SHE IS A MORE ACCOMPLISHED HELMSMAN THAN I WOULD HAVE GIVEN HER CREDIT FOR."

HAIL THE CASPIAN, MISTER DUNBAR. I WANT TO SPEAK WITH CADET HALK.

RIKER

U.S.S. CASPIAN NCC-15507

CAN THIS WAIT, CAPTAIN RIKER? I'M A BIT BUSY RIGHT NOW.

THIS WAS NOT THE PLAN, CADET HALK. YOU WILL RETURN TO THIS SHIP AT ONCE!

"OF COURSE, SIR. INCIDENTALLY, CONGRATULATIONS-- YOU'VE BEATEN THE TIME ALLOTMENT BY ELEVEN MINUTES AND FORTY-ONE SECONDS. I THINK THAT'S A NEW RECORD."

I'LL MEET YOU IN THE TRANSPORTER ROOM, CADET HALK. I THINK WE NEED TO HAVE A TALK.

C'MON NOW, CAPTAIN. WE DID IT, DIDN'T WE?

THAT IS NOT THE POINT, CADET. YOU TOOK AN UNNECESSARY RISK.

WHERE HAVE I HEARD THAT BEFORE...?

CAPTAIN, SICKBAY REPORTS THAT ALMOST ALL THE SURVIVORS HAVE BEEN TRANSPORTED OVER. THE EVACUATION SHOULD BE COMPLETE IN A MATTER OF MINUTES.

"--DAMN. THEY'RE COMING AFTER US NOW!"

THANK YOU, MISTER DATA. THAT IS GOOD--

EVASIVE MANEUVERS, MISTER FARMER. WARP TWO--ENGAGE.

THEY SEEM TO HAVE NO TROUBLE FOLLOWING US.

"READY PHASERS, MISTER THORSLAND..."

OUR PURSUERS ARE FIRING, SIR. IMPACT IN TWO POINT FOUR SECONDS.

...RETURN FIRE!

28

"DIRECT HITS, CAPTAIN. BUT OUR PHASER FIRE SEEMS TO HAVE NO EFFECT."

THEY ARE FIRING ONCE AGAIN, SIR. USING A DIFFERENT WEAPON--SIMILAR TO A PHOTON TORPEDO.

BLAST!

TWO OF OUR SHIELDS ARE DOWN, CAPTAIN. ONE MORE HIT LIKE THE *LAST* ONE WILL DAMAGE THE HULL.

THE SITUATION WOULD NOT BE ANY WORSE-- EXCEPT WE WOULD HAVE TO DISCONTINUE THE EVACUATION.

THE MARCO POLO IS NOT BEING FIRED ON, SIR. NOR ARE WE CONTRIBUTING TO HER DEFENSE.

IF WE WERE TO WITHDRAW--

VERY WELL. MISTER FARMER-- MAKE IT SO!

"THEY ARE DECLINING TO OFFER PURSUIT, CAPTAIN..."

...WHAT IS MORE, THEY ARE COMING ABOUT-- RETURNING TO THEIR ORIGINAL POSITIONS AROUND THE MARCO POLO.

WE ARE NO LONGER OF INTEREST TO THEM. FASCINATING.

APPARENTLY, WE HAVE RETREATED BEYOND THE SPATIAL BOUNDARIES THE SHIPS WERE DESIGNED TO PROTECT.

BUT IF WE HAD INVADED THOSE BOUNDARIES--WHY DID IT TAKE THEM SO LONG TO RESPOND?

THE LIKELIEST POSSIBILITY IS THAT THE SHIPS WERE PROGRAMMED TO PERIODICALLY EXPAND THE REACH OF THEIR SENSOR SCANS. AND WHEN THEY DID SO--THEY DETECTED US.

30

SO IF MISTER LAFORGE CAN GET THE MARCO POLO MOVING AGAIN--ENOUGH TO RETREAT BEYOND THE SHIPS' AREA OF RESPONSIBILITY--

CAPTAIN-- I'M OUT OF TRANSPORTER RANGE.

PICARD TO COMMANDER RIKER.

GO AHEAD, SIR.

THEN WE MAY BE ABLE TO SALVAGE THE VESSEL WITH-OUT FURTHER HOSTILITIES.

YES, MISTER O'BRIEN--I AM AWARE OF THAT.

WE HAVE BEEN ATTACKED BY A COUPLE OF THE SHIPS SURROUNDING YOU--AND FORCED TO PULL BACK. UNFORTUNATELY, WE WERE NO MATCH FOR THEM.

WHEN YOU STOPPED TRANSPORTING, I KNEW SOMETHING WAS WRONG.

...IF YOU CAN GET THE MARCO POLO'S ENGINE WORKING AGAIN, YOU MAY BE HOME FREE. IT SEEMS THAT THE SHIPS FOLLOW THE PRINCIPLES OF TERRITORIALITY-- ONCE AN INTRUDER WITHDRAWS SUFFICIENTLY, IT IS NO LONGER OF CONCERN TO THEM.

BUT WE MAY HAVE GOOD NEWS FOR YOU, NUMBER ONE...

31

I HOPE YOU'RE RIGHT, SIR. IN ANY CASE, I'LL KEEP YOU APPRISED OF OUR PROGRESS.

RIKER OUT.

TRANSFER TUNNEL 8

BEEP!

ANY IDEA HOW LONG IT'S GOING TO TAKE?

HARD TO SAY, COMMANDER.

I'VE GOT TO BYPASS A COUPLE OF DAMAGED TRANSFER TUNNELS--AND THAT COULD TAKE *ONE* HOUR OR SEVERAL.

RIGHT HERE, COMMANDER. SORRY I HAVEN'T CHECKED IN-- BUT YOU CAN REST ASSURED, WE HAVEN'T BEEN GOOFING OFF.

SIR? HAVE YOU GOTTEN ANY WORD REGARDING CAPTAIN HALK?

"MAKE IT CLOSER TO *ONE*, GEORDI. I DON'T TRUST THESE ROBOT SHIPS FOR ONE MINUTE."

U.S.S. MARCO POLO

32

NO, I HAVEN'T. BUT I'M SURE SHE'LL BE FINE...

"...JUST FINE."

WILL RIKER! WHO EXPECTED TO FIND *YOU* HERE?

LYRINDA! HOW IN BLAZES HAVE YOU *BEEN?*

WELL ENOUGH, I GUESS. I HEAR YOU'RE ON THE *HOOD* NOW.

HAVE BEEN FOR A COUPLE OF YEARS. AND YOU'RE ON THE *REPULSE?*

CLOSE. THE *FEARLESS.*

FUNNY HOW WE LOST TOUCH WITH EACH OTHER. WE USED TO BE SO CLOSE.

I GUESS THAT'S WHAT A CAREER WILL DO TO YOU.

I GUESS SO.

33

170

BEAUTIFUL HERE, ISN'T IT?

MORE BEAUTIFUL THAN I REMEMBERED.

HARD TO BELIEVE THAT THESE WERE ONCE THE SHELLS OF LIVING THINGS.

MILLIONS OF YEARS OF EVOLUTION. AND THEN A SUPERNOVA IN A NEIGHBORING SYSTEM WIPES IT ALL OUT. KIND OF SAD WHEN YOU THINK ABOUT IT.

LYRINDA--I'M SORRY.

FOR WHAT?

FOR CHEWING YOU OUT THAT DAY-- WHEN YOU PULLED YOUR CRAZY STUNT AND FLEW THE CASPIAN THROUGH THE METEOR SWARM. I WAS JUST SORE BECAUSE YOU'D DONE IT BEHIND MY BACK.

IF I HADN'T, WE'D HAVE BLOWN THE EXERCISE LIKE EVERYONE ELSE.

THAT WASN'T THE POINT!

THAT'S WHAT YOU SAID THEN. AND I STILL DON'T BUY IT!

34

35

AND JUST WHEN I THOUGHT I'D REALLY IMPRESSED YOU-- REALLY GOTTEN YOUR ATTENTION--YOU CHEW ME OUT AS IF I WERE SOME STRANGER. AS IF WE DIDN'T EVEN *KNOW* EACH OTHER!

THAT'S WHEN I TOLD MYSELF TO FORGET ABOUT YOU. OBVIOUSLY, WE WERE TWO DIFFERENT KINDS OF PEOPLE.

SOME OF US TAKE CHANCES, AND SOME OF US--

WILL--I HOPE YOU'RE NOT DOING THIS OUT OF PITY, BECAUSE--

PITY HAS *NOTHING* TO DO WITH IT.

WILL?

MM?

WHAT ARE YOU TALKING ABOUT? IT FEELS EXACTLY RIGHT. I FEEL SO COMFORTABLE WITH YOU--SO MUCH AT EASE.

ME, TOO. BUT IT'S NOT THAT SIMPLE ANYMORE.

I DON'T KNOW IF THIS IS SUCH A GOOD IDEA.

IT CAN BE.

WE'VE GOT OUR CAREERS TO THINK OF NOW.

THERE ARE PEOPLE WITH RELATIONSHIPS IN STARFLEET. LOTS OF THEM!

BUT A SHIP CAN HAVE ONLY ONE CAPTAIN--AND THAT WOULD REQUIRE ONE OF US TO MAKE A COMPROMISE.

ARE YOU GOING TO BE THE ONE?

"GOOD-BYE, WILL."

COMMANDER-- WE'VE GOT THOSE TRANSFER TUNNELS BACK ON LINE!

EXCELLENT, MISTER LAFORGE!

AT THIS POINT, WE'RE JUST CLEANING UP SOME LOOSE ENDS. WE SHOULD HAVE THE ENGINES BACK UP AND RUNNING IN A MATTER OF MINUTES!

THAT'S GREAT NEWS, GEORDI!

WHAT'S YOUR NAME, CREWMAN?

I THOUGHT YOU'D LIKE IT. AND AFTER WE FINISH HERE, WE'LL SEE IF WE CAN'T GET THE SENSORS BACK ON LINE.

BRETT, SIR. DAVID BRETT.

TAKE THE OPS STATION, MISTER BRETT. WE'RE GOING TO NEED ALL THE HELP WE CAN GET.

DOCTOR CRUSHER-- I NEED YOU TO SECURE YOUR PATIENTS. WE'LL BE HITTING THE ROAD IN A FEW MINUTES, AND IT'S LIABLE TO BE A ROUGH RIDE.

WHAT BRINGS YOU HERE, CAPTAIN PICARD?

TO SEE HOW YOU'RE COMING ALONG, OF COURSE.

AND ALSO TO LET YOU KNOW--MY CHIEF ENGINEER HAS REPAIRED YOUR PROPULSION SYSTEM. COMMANDER RIKER WILL BE ATTEMPTING TO ESCAPE YOUR MYSTERIOUS ASSAILANTS.

I HOPE HE DOES A BETTER JOB THAN I DID.

SCRATCH THAT. I KNOW HE WILL! YOUR COMMANDER RIKER IS THE BEST...

...HE PLAYS IT BY THE BOOK-- NOT LIKE YOURS TRULY.

INTERESTING. IT APPEARS THAT THE SHIPS ARE PROGRAMMED TO RESPOND TO DIFFERENT INTRUDERS IN DIFFERENT WAYS--PERHAPS ACCORDING TO THEIR SIZE OR--

NOT NOW, DATA. WE'VE GOT TO GIVE COMMANDER RIKER SOME BREATHING ROOM.

"IF WE CAN'T STOP THEM, WE CAN AT LEAST BE A THORN IN THEIR SIDES. READY PHOTON TORPEDOES...

"...FIRE!"

THEY ARE *RETURNING* FIRE, CAPTAIN.

"SHIELDS ARE GONE, SIR-- TORN APART. AND WE'VE GOT A HULL BREACH ON DECK ELEVEN."

DAMN! WE HAVEN'T SLOWED THEM DOWN ONE *IOTA!*

45

IT SEEMS YOU ARE ON YOUR OWN, NUMBER ONE! NOTHING WE DO SEEMS TO DAUNT THEM.

...IF THE ROBOT SHIPS HAVE A WEAKNESS, IT'S *MANEUVERABILITY.* I'VE BEEN TIMING THEIR RESPONSES TO OUR COURSE CHANGES, AND IT TAKES THEM A FULL SECOND TO REACT--A SECOND WHICH THEY MAKE UP WITH THEIR ABILITY TO ACCELERATE.

"...THE PHENOMENON WE ENCOUNTERED EARLIER, SIR--THE LONG, STRING-LIKE BLACK HOLES--I THINK WE CAN USE THEM TO OUR ADVANTAGE..."

THAT'S ALL RIGHT, SIR. I JUST THOUGHT OF SOMETHING...

IF WE WERE TO WEAVE A PATH THROUGH THOSE *SUPER STRINGS...* OUR PURSUERS MIGHT NOT BE ABLE TO MAKE THE REQUIRED COURSE CHANGES IN TIME.

IT'S DANGEROUS, NUMBER ONE. THOSE SUPER STRINGS, AS YOU CALL THEM, ARE NOT EXACTLY STANDING STILL.

"I KNOW, SIR. WE MAY NOT HAVE THE MANEUVERABILITY TO MAKE IT THROUGH, EITHER. BUT IF THE ALTERNATIVE IS TO BE *BLASTED* TO BITS..."

UH-OH. THERE GO THE TRANSFER TUNNELS AGAIN. LOOKS LIKE WE PUSHED THEM A LITTLE TOO HARD.

·THEY LASTED LONG ENOUGH. THAT'S WHAT COUNTS.

TROUBLE, NUMBER ONE? I SEE YOU'VE DROPPED OUT OF WARP.

NOTHING WE CAN'T HANDLE, SIR.

PERHAPS YOU'D BETTER LET THE OTHERS HANDLE IT, COMMANDER. DOCTOR CRUSHER MAY NEED SOME HELP TRANSPORTING THE REMAINDER OF THE MARCO POLO'S CREW TO OUR SICKBAY.

AYE, SIR. I'D LIKE TO CHECK IN ON ONE OF THE PATIENTS THERE MYSELF.

GOOD IDEA, COMMANDER.

"I THINK YOU WILL FIND THAT SHE IS EXPECTING YOU."

WILL!

IN THE FLESH-- THANKS TO MISTER WORF'S EXPERTISE AT THE HELM.

FLOWERS? HOW SWEET OF YOU.

NOT EXACTLY WHAT I WAS LOOKING FOR-- BUT THEN, OUR ABRBORETUM ISN'T EQUIPPED FOR FRESH EIDELWEISS.

I HEARD ABOUT WHAT YOU DID OUT THERE. YOU TOOK QUITE A CHANCE.

WHEN DID YOU BECOME SUCH A RISK-TAKER?

LET'S JUST SAY I HAD A GOOD TEACHER-- AND LEAVE IT AT THAT.

YOU KNOW, IT'S FUNNY. JUST A SHORT WHILE AGO, I WAS TELLING YOUR CAPTAIN THAT I'D TAKEN ONE RISK TOO MANY. THAT I SHOULD HAVE LISTENED TO YOU WAY BACK WHEN.

53